None
of These
Diseases

BY S. I. McMillen, M.D.

None of These Diseases
Discern These Times

None of These Diseases

S.I.McMillen

Marshall Pickering

Marshall Morgan & Scott
Marshall Pickering
34–42 Cleveland Street, London W1P 5FB

First published by Fleming H. Revell Co. in the United States of America
This edition published in the UK by Marshall Morgan & Scott, 1984
Reprinted 1989

British Library CIP Data

McMillen, S. I.
      None of these diseases
      1. Pathology   2. Medicine
      I. Title
      616   RB111

      ISBN 0-551-01159-9

Reproduced, printed and bound in Great Britain by
BPCC Hazell Books Ltd
Member of BPCC Ltd
Aylesbury, Bucks, England

To
A MOTHER
A SISTER
A WIFE
A DAUGHTER
A GRANDDAUGHTER-IN-LAW

Contents

Foreword

Spanning two decades since the publication of its first edition, hundreds of thousands of copies of *None of These Diseases* have appeared on the shelves of bookstores, libraries, churches, and homes throughout the world.

Describing the biblical way to health and well-being, this book has provided insight and inspiration—year in and year out—to its thousands of readers, many of whom discovered for the first time the extraordinary medical benefits that they could obtain simply by heeding God's Word.

Perhaps this book was so popular because author S. I. McMillen—medical doctor, missionary, college professor, and Bible scholar—accepted the challenge of writing about profound subjects in a way that could be easily understood by old and young people, scholarly and unlearned minds, mature and newborn Christians, and even by those who had never come to know Christ.

Did he accomplish his task? Soon after publication, *None of These Diseases* appeared on best-seller lists throughout the United States and Canada. . . . It remained a best-seller for many years. . . . Book reviewers, leading periodicals, and book clubs featured the book. . . . It was translated into more foreign languages than any other title published by our century-old firm. . . . It appeared in different editions: hard binding, paper binding, gift binding; in large print and in Braille. . . . Various chapters were featured separately in booklets and periodicals.

Its global distribution of over one million copies and its life-changing impact on countless readers attest to the fact that, with God's help, Dr. McMillen was eminently successful in writing just the right book at just the right time.

Anxiously awaited by the book trade, the Christian media, and the reading public is this revised, updated, and expanded edition of *None of These Diseases*. The editorial work on this new edition was ably accomplished by Dr. McMillen's grandson, David Stern, who is currently completing his studies at Jefferson Medical College in Philadelphia.

Rather than just producing a glossed-over new edition of the same book, David has revised every chapter and has also taken on some new challenges. With originality, he reveals new medical evidence in support of the inspiration of Scripture; with frankness, he discusses the issue of homosexuality; in detail, he explains newly publicized diseases such as AIDS and herpes; and with Scripture, he supports the new scientific theories for coping with emotional stress. Containing over 200 new references, 60 new pages, and 20 new illustrations—these chapters attest to the fact that this new edition is innovative, inspirational, scholarly, and up-to-date.

It is our special privilege to present to the public this fascinating new edition, and it is our special prayer that this new edition will help to meet the needs of current-day readers. Thus, we are confident that *None of These Diseases* will have a continuing ministry-in-print for a long, long time to come.

THE PUBLISHERS

Memoir

Dr. S. I. McMillen was born in Barnesboro, Pennsylvania, on March 23, 1898, to the wife of a local physician. Barnesboro was a coal-mining town with a saloon on almost every intersection within the city limits. Saturday nights after the miners received their pay, they filled the bars with loud guffaws and drunken brawls. As a young boy, "Guy" or "Hey You"—appellations they gave the young McMillen because his parents had never bothered to name him—often visited the bars to hassle the bartender until the man would give the lad a pretzel. He still remembers witnessing a particular fight where a gang of inebriated miners kicked the head of another miner until he was completely unconscious.

At the age of eight, "Hey You" decided that he needed a name, and he chose initials that spelled his first name—Sim. A middle name of Isocrates seemed logical to the young lad. Thus, it is not surprising that as an adult he was known to his friends as simply "Mac" or "Dr. Mac."

On a rare Sunday, Sim accompanied his mother to a Baptist church where the people customarily shouted and danced in the aisles. His father, as a young man, had been a fervent Christian who had been very active in a local church where he had even held office. As the years passed, however, his Sunday mornings and many other mornings became times to recover from the drinking binges of the night before. Drunk, he often became violent; and at one time or another, he physically abused every member of the family.

One night, Sim's older sister, Oneida, came to know the Lord at a camp meeting. When she told her father, he became furious and tried to dissuade her. As a member of the Wesleyan Methodist Church, Oneida grew quickly in the knowledge of the Lord; and she soon decided to become a pastor in the church (the Wesleyans were one of the first denominations to allow women to preach). When her father heard that she planned to go to Faulkener, New York, to become a preacher, he became furious and cursed her through cigar smoke: "All right you can go. But if you die up there, let them bury you up there. I don't ever want to see your face again." Penniless, Oneida left her family and job; and took a job as an assistant pastor in Faulkener.

11

Sim's father soon suffered the consequences of his constant smoking, binge drinking, and negative emotions. He became stricken with cirrhosis of the liver. Suffering multiple strokes, he needed a cane just to shuffle his way across a room. At the age of fifty-five, he was forced to discontinue the practice of medicine. Without financial support, the family had to sell their house and move to Faulkener where they lived in the parsonage of the church that Oneida now pastored. In the home of his hated daughter, Sim's father was tenderly nursed until he died of a massive stroke.

Sim attended some of his sister's revival services, and he soon came to accept the Lord—an experience that is described in this book. He graduated from Faulkener High School in 1915 and spent the next year at a local teacher-training school, a logical next step since tuition was free and he could live at home. In 1917, he taught twenty-five children, grades one through eight, in the one-room schoolhouse of a nearby town, Gerry. There he earned $50 per month. He visited Faulkener on weekends to teach Sunday school, and in the winter he made the commute in a horse-drawn sleigh through the deserted winter wonderland of Western New York.

In 1918, he entered Fredonia State Teacher Training College where tuition was also free. He paid for his room and board with his savings from the previous year and generous donations from his sister. From 1918 to 1922, he acted as principal of Cassadaga High School and then taught science at Faulkener High School.

Using his meager savings, he moved to Chicago in the summer of 1922. While attending the University of Chicago, he got three meals a day at a Chinese restaurant in return for working four hours a day as a waiter. He finished his premedical studies in four semesters, and applied to three medical schools—Harvard, Johns Hopkins, and the University of Pennsylvania. He was accepted at all three schools; and in the fall, he matriculated at the University of Pennsylvania. If he could obtain one of the two highest scores in his medical-school class on a science examination, he would receive a full scholarship for the full four years. This was his only reasonable hope to pay the $400 per year tuition, so he threw himself into studying for the exam. God rewarded his hard work, and he received one of the two scholarships in his class. While in medical school, the Wesleyan Methodist Church supported him with a small grant; and he worked summers at various jobs, including riveting submarine doors to their moorings, unloading cement bags from boxcars, and nailing rafters as a carpenter's assistant.

In 1926, he married the Dean of Women at Houghton College, Alice Jean Hampe, the daughter of a Wesleyan pastor who founded eight churches during his ministry. In 1927, Dr. McMillen started his internship at the Bryn Mawr Hospital in a suburb of Philadelphia. He chose this internship because it was one of the few that paid a salary at that time—a salary of $50 a month. Back then interns were overworked even more than they are now, and his schedule entailed thirty-six hours on with twelve hours off—leaving only one night in two for catching up on sleep and visiting with his wife.

In 1928, the couple signed up for missionary service with the Wesleyan Church. For the initial six months, Dr. McMillen studied at the London School of Tropical Medicine. Then the Wesleyan Church sent them to Sierra Leone, Africa. During one of their four three-year terms, they traveled on a motorcycle into the jungles of Sierra Leone where Dr. McMillen supervised the building of a new missionary hospital. The Kamakwe Mission Hospital compound included ten buildings, some of which are still used today. During their second furlough, Linda (David's mother), was born to Mrs. McMillen.

Working in the tropics, Dr. McMillen treated many severe and lethal diseases. For example, one day a woman brought her small child to the hospital. She had recently become a Christian so, despite the protestations of her family and friends, she had refused to go to the tribal witch doctor. Instead, she had brought her child to the missionary hospital. When Dr. McMillen heard her story and looked at the foul-smelling and rapidly spreading ulcer on the child's cheek, he was greatly distressed. Most patients waited until the witch doctor had failed before coming for the "white man's" medicine, yet here was a woman with such an unusual faith in God that she had come to the missionary doctor first. This child had noma, an ulcer that was completely untreatable and quickly ate into the victim's brain, killing over 90 percent of its victims. It appeared that this woman's faith would soon become a laughingstock of the local tribe.

That night as he lay in bed, Dr. McMillen could not sleep. After tossing for several hours, he fervently prayed that the Lord would give him a way to cure this child. Instantly, the Lord answered his prayer. Of course! Noma was caused by a combination of bacteria, namely *Spirochaeta vincenti* and *Bacillus fusiformis*—the same two bacteria that caused tropical ulcer. Tropical ulcer was easily treated by applying a solution of formaldehyde to the ulcer. Maybe this same treatment would also cure noma. He rushed down to the hospital. After stuffing the child's mouth and nostrils with cotton, he applied the formaldehyde solution to the child's cheek. Within days, the lethal ulcer stopped spreading, the dead tissue fell off, and the cheek healed almost completely. The Lord had rewarded the woman's faith. If she had gone to the witch doctor first, her child would have surely died; instead, her child was the first successfully treated case of noma.

During the next few years, Dr. McMillen was able to successfully treat six more cases of noma. These cases were reported in the *American Journal of Diseases of Children* (volume 50 [December 1935]:1495–1496; volume 62 [September, 1941]:590–595).

When World War II broke out, the family of three left Africa on one of the last freighters to leave the country. Leaving seemed impossible, but the Lord provided a ship that needed a physician. Halfway across the Atlantic and in the middle of a dark night, the ship was hailed by a German submarine. The German soldiers boarded the ship and searched it for munitions. The ship had none, so they allowed it to continue.

In 1942, Mrs. McMillen accepted an invitation to return to Houghton College to teach Bible, and Dr. McMillen accepted a position as college physician. He soon started a busy practice, and he taught a class on missions at the college. A traditional family doctor, he made house calls within a thirty-mile radius of Houghton. His son-in-law, Dr. James M. Stern (David's father), took over the practice for a year in 1962, enabling Dr. McMillen to write the first edition of *None of These Diseases*.

Dr. McMillen retired from medicine in 1967. During his early retirement, he wrote a book on prophecy entitled, *Discern These Times*. Traveling throughout the country, he carried the message that the fulfillment of prophecies and the discoveries of medicine were constantly providing evidence for the veracity of the Word of God.

Dr. and Mrs. McMillen still reside next to the campus of Houghton College where he can be seen briskly walking every morning at 6:30 A.M. He is currently writing another book, *You Can Be Sure*.

His grandson, David Stern, graduated from Houghton College where he lived with Dr. and Mrs. McMillen. While finishing up his studies at Jefferson Medical College in Philadelphia, David revised this book. His physician wife, Diane, is a resident in pathology; and her suggestions made a significant contribution to this revised edition.

D.E.S.

Preface

Inner peace does not come in time-release capsules. How sad! If pills brought peace, physicians could purge mankind of a host of diseases provoked by emotional turmoil—turmoil resulting from fear, envy, resentment, hatred, and other carnal emotions.

Emotional stress can irritate or precipitate heart attacks, strokes, ulcers, asthma, and many other diseases. As physicians, we can prescribe medicines to palliate the symptoms, but we can do little to eradicate the underlying cause—emotional turmoil.

No pill can still the emotional uproar of the man who just squandered his life's savings, the woman who just discovered her husband's infidelity, or the teenager who just demolished his father's car.

This book is the fruit ripened by a thousand sighs for our many patients who left the office or hospital without receiving adequate help. We describe many such patients in this book, but their identities have been carefully disguised with fictitious names and altered circumstances. We seldom had time to do more than prescribe a few pills for their most pressing symptoms; but when time permitted, we prescribed something far more effective than any medications. In this book, we summarize this prescription; we say "summarize" because the original prescription was written several thousand years ago.

After God led the Israelites out of Egypt, He promised His people that if they would obey His statutes, He would put *"none of these diseases"* upon them. Was this a trustworthy promise? Could submitting to a code of "restrictive" rules lead to freedom from sicknesses? Could this promise remain pertinent even in the twentieth century?

Yes! Medical science is still discovering how obedience to the ancient prescriptions saved the primitive Hebrews from the scourges of epidemic plagues; and medical research is constantly proving the timeless potency of the divine prescription for modern diseases. Yes! Obedience to biblical precepts is still the most effective way to prevent many of the afflictions of mankind.

Peace does not come in capsules. Peace can only come from the source of peace, who said to His disciples: "Peace I leave with you,

15

my peace I give unto you: not as the world giveth, give I unto you. Let not your heart be troubled . . ." (John 14:27 KJV).

We pray that God will use this book to help you discover, claim, and experience God's prescription for your health and peace.

S.I.M.
D.E.S.

None
of These
Diseases

Chapter One

Gray Hair and Rattlesnake Oil

 "To prevent the hair from turning gray, anoint it with the blood of a black calf which has been boiled in oil, or with the fat of a rattlesnake."[1] This prescription comes from the famous *Ebers Papyrus*, a medical book written in Egypt about 1552 B.C. Since Egypt occupied the dominant position in the ancient medical world, the *Ebers Papyrus* gives us a record of the most advanced medical knowledge of that day.

The book also contains prescriptions for people who are losing hair. "When it falls out, one remedy is to apply a mixture of six fats, namely those of the horse, the hippopotamus, the crocodile, the cat, the snake, and the ibex. To strengthen it, anoint with the tooth of a donkey crushed in honey."[2] An extraspecial dressing for the Egyptian Queen Schesch consisted of equal parts of a heel of an Abyssinian greyhound, date blossoms, and asses' hoofs—all boiled in oil. The choice preparation was intended to make the royal hair grow.

To save victims bitten by poisonous snakes, physicians of that day gave them "magic water" to drink—water that had been poured over a special idol.[3] To embedded splinters they applied worms' blood and asses' dung. Since dung is loaded with tetanus

19

spores, it is little wonder that lockjaw took a heavy toll of splinter cases.

Several hundred remedies for diseases are advised in the *Ebers Papyrus*. In their drugs they mixed such things as: dust-of-a-statue, shell-of-a-beetle, head-of-the-electric-eel, guts-of-the-goose, tail-of-a-mouse, fat-of-the-hippopotamus, hair-of-a-cat, eyes-of-a-pig, toes-of-a-dog, milk-of-a-woman, and semen-of-a-man.[4]

About the time this Egyptian medical textbook was written, Moses was born in Egypt. Although his parents were Hebrews, he was raised in Pharaoh's royal court and "was educated in all the wisdom of the Egyptians."[5] There is little doubt that he was well acquainted with the medical knowledge of his time. Many thousands of the Israelites also knew and no doubt had used some of the common remedies mentioned in the *Ebers Papyrus*.

When Moses led the Israelites out of Egypt, however, God made a most remarkable covenant with the new nation: "If thou wilt diligently hearken to the voice of the Lord thy God, and wilt do that which is right in his sight, and wilt give ear to his commandments, and keep all his statutes, *I will put none of these diseases upon thee*, which I have brought upon the Egyptians: for I am the Lord that healeth thee" (Exodus 15:26 KJV).

"None of these diseases . . ."! What a promise! Had not the Egyptians and Israelites been afflicted with epidemics for ages? The remedies in their medical books had accomplished practically nothing; often the "cure" was worse than the disease. Yet, here the Lord made a fantastic promise to free the Israelites from epidemics of the Egyptian diseases.

God proceeded to give Moses a number of commandments, which form part of our Bible today. Because these medical directions were altogether different from those in the *Ebers Papyrus*, God surely was not copying from the medical authorities of the day. Would Moses, trained in the royal postgraduate universities, have enough faith to accept the divine innovations without adding some of the things he had been taught? From the record, we discover that Moses had so much faith in God's regulations that he did not incorporate a single current medical misconception into the inspired instructions. If Moses had yielded to a natural inclination to add even a little of his modern university training, we would be reading such prescriptions as "the heel of an Abyssinian greyhound" or "the tooth of a donkey crushed in honey"—not to mention the drugs the leading physicians were compounding out of the bacteria-laden dung of dogs, cats, and flies.

The divine instructions were not only devoid of harmful practices, but had many detailed positive recommendations. Let us take a glance at the impact of those positive instructions on the history of infectious-disease control.

For many hundreds of years the dreaded disease leprosy had killed and maimed countless millions of people in Europe. The extent of the horrible malady among Europeans is described by Dr. George Rosen, Columbia University emeritus professor of public health:

> Leprosy cast the greatest blight that threw its shadow over the daily life of medieval humanity. Fear of all other diseases taken together can hardly be compared to the terror spread by leprosy. Not even the Black Death in the fourteenth century or the appearance of syphilis toward the end of the fifteenth century produced a similar state of fright. . . . Early in the Middle Ages, during the sixth and seventh centuries, it began to spread more widely in Europe and became a serious social and health problem. It was endemic particularly among the poor and reached a terrifying peak in the thirteenth and fourteenth centuries.[6]

What did the physicians offer to stop the ever-increasing ravages of leprosy? Some taught that it was brought on by eating spiced food, spoiled fish, or diseased pork. Other physicians said it was caused by "malign conjunction of the planets." Naturally, their suggestions for prevention were utterly worthless.

What brought the leprosy epidemic of the Dark Ages under control? George Rosen gives us the answer:

> Leadership was taken by the church, as the physicians had nothing to offer. The church took as its guiding principle the concept of contagion as embodied in the Old Testament. . . . This idea and its practical consequences are defined with great clarity in the book of Leviticus. . . . Once the condition of leprosy had been established, the patient was to be segregated and excluded from the community.
>
> Following the precepts laid down in Leviticus the church undertook the task of combatting leprosy . . . it accomplished the first great feat . . . in methodical eradication of disease.[7]

The procedures came from Leviticus 13:46. "As long as he has the infection he remains unclean. He must live alone; he must live outside the camp" (NIV). Although the "leprosy" of the Bible was much more ravaging than the modern disease we call "leprosy" and although it may actually have been a completely different disease, the biblical method for control of infectious skin diseases is unequaled in the history of ancient man.

Other historians credit the Bible for the dawning of a new era in the effective control of disease: "The laws against leprosy in Leviticus 13 may be regarded as the first model of a sanitary legislation."[8]

In Norway, however, "The decrease in the incidence of the disease led to the relaxing of precautions, and the disease again appeared in those parts of the country where it had not been completely eradicated."[9] Lepers even went from door to door selling their wares. In view of the fact that the bacterium that causes leprosy is found in very high concentrations in the secretions within the nose, it is no wonder that this practice promoted the spread of leprosy.[10] Because of the widespread belief that leprosy was hereditary, people did not fear that they could "catch" it from lepers. But in 1873, Dr. Armauer Hansen propelled the study of leprosy out of the Dark Ages of conjecture when he identified the bacterium that causes leprosy. This discovery proved that leprosy was a contagious disease; and three years later, the Norwegian Leprosy Act was passed. This law ordered lepers to live in precautionary isolation away from their families. In 1856, there were 2,858 lepers living in Norway. By the turn of the century, only 577 lepers were left; and that number plummeted to 69. By 1930 the spectacular discoveries of science allowed Norway to control this disease, but the precautions taken had been written down by Moses almost 3,500 years earlier.

The health of thousands was greatly improved because men began to practice the words of God to the Israelites. Thus, they experienced the promise of God: "If thou wilt diligently hearken to the voice of the Lord thy God . . . I will put *none of these diseases* upon thee. . . ."

Chapter Two

Pride and Prejudice Versus Proof

 Although Europe brought the devastations of leprosy under control by obeying the biblical injunction to isolate the victims, other preventable diseases continued to decimate mankind. Intestinal diseases such as cholera, dysentery, and typhoid fever continued to take many lives. Up to the close of the eighteenth century, hygienic provisions, even in the great capitals, were quite primitive. It was the rule for excrement to be dumped into the streets, which were unpaved and filthy. Powerful stenches gripped villages and cities. It was a heyday for flies as they bred in the filth and spread intestinal diseases that killed millions.

Such waste of human lives could have been prevented if Europe had only taken seriously God's provision for freeing man of diseases. With a single sentence the Bible pointed the way to deliverance from the deadly epidemics of typhoid, cholera, and dysentery: "Designate a place outside the camp where you can go to relieve yourself. As part of your equipment have something to dig with, and when you relieve yourself, dig a hole and cover up your excrement" (Deuteronomy 23:12,13 NIV).

A medical historian writes that this directive is "certainly a primitive measure, but an effective one, which indicates advanced ideas of sanitation."[1] How could this recommendation offer such advanced ideas of sanitation, since the theory of infectious spread of disease was not developed until 3,500 years later? Despite recent attempts to credit this knowledge to the benevolent teachings of visiting extraterrestrials or to the incredible genius of Moses, a simpler and more reasonable explanation is that this record is what it claims to be: Moses' recording of God's words.

But the pride and prejudices of man are often foes too strong for proof. Let me give an example by citing what happened in Vienna in the 1840s, when the Viennese were dancing to the superb waltzes of Johann Strauss.

Vienna was also famous as a medical center. Let us look in on one of the famous teaching hospitals of that day, Allegemeine Kraken-haus. In the maternity wards of this celebrated hospital, one out of every six women died; and this frightening mortality rate was similar in other hospitals around the world. The obstetricians ascribed the deaths to unremitting constipation, delayed lactation, excessive fear, and poisonous air. Because of their ignorance of the cause, their ideas for prevention proved useless.

When the women died, their bodies were wheeled into the autopsy room. Each morning, as their first order of business, the physicians and medical students entered the hospital morgue to perform autopsies on the unfortunate victims who had died during the preceding twenty-four hours. Afterward, without washing their hands, the attending doctors and medical students marched into the maternity wards to perform pelvic examinations on the living women. Of course, no rubber gloves were worn.

In the early 1840s a young doctor named Ignaz Semmelweis was given charge over one of the obstetrical wards. He observed that those women who were examined became sick and died much more often than the women who were not examined. After watching this heartbreaking situation for three years, he established a new rule for his ward. He ordered every physician and medical student who had participated in autopsies of the dead to carefully wash his hands before examining living maternity patients.

In April 1847, before the new rule went into effect, fifty-seven (or one out of six) women had died in Dr. Semmelweis's ward. Then he instituted the hand-washing rule. In June, only one out of every forty-two women died; in July, only one out of every eighty-four——a fourteenfold decrease in mortality. These astonishing statistics strongly indicated that fatal infections had been carried from corpses to living patients.

One day, after performing autopsies and washing their hands, the physicians and students entered the maternity ward and examined a row of beds containing twelve women. Eleven of the twelve women quickly developed temperatures and died.

Another new thought was born in Semmelweis's alert brain: some mysterious element was evidently carried from one living patient to others, and with fatal consequences. Logically, Semmelweis ordered that everybody wash his hands carefully after examining each living patient. Immediately, howls of protest were raised against the "nuisance" of washing, washing, washing; but the mortality rate went further down.

Was Semmelweis acclaimed by his fellows? To the contrary—lazy students, prejudiced obstetricians, and jealous superiors scorned and belittled him so much that he was dismissed from the hospital. His successor threw out the wash basins, and up shot the mortality rate to the old terrifying figures. Were his colleagues convinced then? Not at all! Even the world-renowned pathologist Rudolf Virchow continued to ridicule Semmelweis. We mortals might as well face it; our heads are so hardened by pride and prejudice that proof can rarely penetrate them.

For eight months Semmelweis tried to regain a respectable position in the hospital, but to no avail. Shocked and depressed, he left Vienna without saying good-bye to his few friends. In Budapest, he obtained a position in a local hospital where the mortality rate of pregnant women was also frightful. Again, he instituted the practice of hand washing. At once the grim reaper was halted. But again prejudices and jealousies blinded his colleagues to the proof, and many of them passed him in the hospital corridors without speaking.

Dr. Semmelweis wrote an excellently documented book on his work, which only spurred his assailants to the bitterest sarcasm. The constant strain of jeering physicians plus the death cries of dying mothers so haunted and weighed on his sensitive nature that his mind finally broke. Ignaz Semmelweis was committed to a mental institution. There he died, ironically, of a blood infection without ever receiving the recognition he richly deserved.

Today, medicine recognizes the work of Semmelweis as among the greatest advances in the practice of medicine. A 1982 medical textbook declares, "Routine hand-washing before, between, and after contact with patients is recognized as the most important feature of successful infection control."[2]

Many centuries before Semmelweis, however, God gave to Moses detailed instructions on the safest method for cleansing the hands after handling the dead or the infected living.[3] Semmelweis's method of cleansing went a long way in preventing many deaths, but it would not be accepted in any hospital today. Dr. Allen Steere of the Centers for Disease Control has outlined the proper modern method for washing hands: "The hands should be vigorously lathered and rubbed together for at least 15 seconds under a moderate-sized stream of water. . . . There is no good substitute for routine handwashing with soap and running water."[4] Agreeing with and expanding on these recommendations, the scriptural method specified not merely washing in a basin, but repeated washings in running water with time intervals allowed for drying and exposure to sun to kill bacteria not washed off. The soap used is even more remarkable. It was made by burning together in a fire the following: a young cow, cedar wood, hyssop branches, and scarlet wool. The washing solution contained an irritant, cedar-wood oil, that would encourage scrubbing; an antiseptic, hyssop oil, that would kill bacteria and fungi; and a scrubbing element, wool fibers, that would dislodge the bacteria. Even today, hospitals often use a similar granular soap because, as Dr. Steere states, "It is difficult to remove granular soap from the hands in less than 15 seconds. Thus, the use of a dry soap preparation may provide a mechanism for reminding [hospital] personnel of an adequate length of time for routine handwashing."[5]

According to the scriptural method, wet branches of hyssop were used to shower soapy water on the unclean person. Most authorities feel that hyssop refers to a type of marjoram plant that grows in the Middle East. The sweet-smelling oil of marjoram is still used in perfumes, and it contains about 50 percent carvacrol. Carvacrol is almost identical to thymol, an antifungal and antibacterial agent that is still used in the practice of medicine.

Anyone who had touched a dead person was required to remain separate from the people for a whole week. If the dead person had died from an infectious disease, this week of quarantine would usually allow ample time for a person contaminated by contact to come down with the disease. Thus, these regulations prevented rampant spread of disease among the Israelites.

Furthermore, the scriptural method also required contacts to change into clothes that had been washed and dried. The biblical technique is so different from and so much more effective than anything man devised until this century that, again, it seems logical that the regulations were given, as the Bible claims, from God to Moses.

The spirit of pride and prejudice regarding the washing of hands also existed in surgery. During most of the nineteenth century the preliminaries of major surgery were frightfully simple. The patient went into the operating room, took off his trousers and underwear, and crawled up on the operating table. The surgeon took off his coat, rolled up his sleeves, removed some instruments from a bag, and started to operate. If the surgeon wished his students to examine something inside the opening, he would have them step forward and poke their germ-covered hands into a previously sterile abdomen.

Of course, the mortality from surgery was frightful. Dr. Roswell Park tells about his own experiences in his book on medical history: "When I began my work, in 1876, as a hospital interne, in one of the largest hospitals in this country, it happened that during my first winter's experience, with but one or two exceptions, every patient operated upon in that hospital, and that by men who were esteemed the peers of anyone in their day, died of blood poisoning. . . ."[6]

Such mortality would not have occurred if the surgeons had only followed the method God gave to Moses regarding the meticulous method of washing and changing of clothes.

Dr. Park states that in the two years following 1876, the year that the antiseptic method of cleansing hands and instruments was implemented, there was a spectacular drop in the mortality rate. The work of John Tyndall, Louis Pasteur, Robert Koch, and Sir Joseph Lister finally furnished visible proof that slowly dispelled pride and prejudice.

In the twentieth century no surgical procedure is performed without meticulous scrubbing of the hands. However, failure to wash the hands carefully when treating medical cases still results in needless loss of lives.

Every day in every large hospital in the world people die because of infections that they get while in the hospital. There is no doubt that hand washing is the most important method for controlling these infections. Even today, many doctors ignore this fact and do not wash their hands after contact with each patient. A decade ago, my son-in-law, David's father, completed his surgical residency at a large university hospital. Doing surgery, he recognized the importance of cleanliness, and he implemented extraordinarily rigorous standards of cleanliness for surgical procedures. His infection rate for surgery was much lower than that of his superior doctors and fellow residents, so one would have expected them to change their standards of cleanliness. Following the example of Dr. Semmelweis's colleagues, however, they made fun of the new, bothersome procedures. At the conclusion of his residency, they bestowed him with the title "Dr. Clean" and gave him an honorary trophy, a bar of soap.

A very thorough study done in West Germany demonstrates the prevalence of hospital-acquired infections. After performing autopsies on 1,000 patients, doctors found 137 patients who had acquired infections while in the hospital and 74 deaths that were a direct result of these infections.[7]

Newborn infants with their immature immune systems are especially susceptible to infections. Several years ago, someone noticed an outbreak of infections within the nursery at Boston City Hospital.

During this outbreak, eleven newborn infants came down with infections and four died. Doctors searched for the source of infection and soon found it, the contaminated hands of a single nurse.[8]

Even in the twentieth century doctors keep rediscovering—at a frightful cost—the necessity of hand washing: a principle that God gave to Moses 3,500 years ago.

Chapter Three

Robber of Ten Million Brains

 When my phone rang about midnight, I was very sleepy, but the voice on the other end aroused me instantly. "Doc, come out here right away! Two people were killed on Route 19, and two others are in desperate shape!"

A crowd was there when I arrived. The driver had hit a bridge abutment, and the steering wheel had flattened his chest. One look at him showed me that he was beyond human help. The three passengers had hurtled thirty feet through the windshield into a dry creek bed. One of them, a woman, was dead. A second woman was lying on the crumpled windshield that she took with her as she was propelled forward. She was moaning with pain. A semiconscious man also lay in the mud and gravel of the creek.

What an unforgettable scene of devastation: the telescoped car mashed against the bridge, two mangled people covered with blood, and two screaming bodies silenced by death. The horror of the catastrophe was particularly pathetic because it could have been prevented. All of the victims probably would have walked away from the accident if they had been wearing seat belts. Furthermore, the accident never would have occurred if the brain of the driver had not been robbed by a drug. Unused safety belts and a shattered whiskey bottle testified to the inanity of the tragedy.

29

That ghastly night, I saw the destruction, suffering, and death that can result when alcohol robs the brain of a car driver. My mind is much too small to multiply the scenes of greater and lesser magnitude that occur daily because the brains of over 10 million Americans are thus robbed.

What percentage of the 46,000 annual highway deaths is caused by partially decerebrated Americans? Studies have shown that up to 64 percent of these accidents involves alcohol.[1] An astounding 92 percent of drivers involved in fatal single-car accidents have had something to drink. During the twelve years of the Vietnam war, 46,483 American soldiers died. In the past twelve years, however, alcohol has claimed the lives of over 300,000 Americans on our nation's highways. Why haven't we seen protest rallies about this unnecessary slaughter?

In our country, John Barleycorn's annual mass murder of over 25,000 Americans stands as a tremendous indictment against our government, industry, and culture. Many a driver has had his license revoked for causing one wanton death on the highway, yet here is one who is legally licensed to liquidate thousands.

What part do these 10 million alcohol abusers play in other types of violent deaths, such as homicide? I shall never forget the night I entered a house to find a drunken man pressing a cocked revolver against the temple of his wife, the mother of his five children. It was fortunate that I arrived when I did. Perhaps it was my presence that made him release her; but as he did, he told his wife, "If I didn't think I'd hang for this, I'd blow your brains out."

Statistical studies reveal that alcohol plays a prominent role in almost every type of crime. Fifty-three percent of murders, 57 percent of sex crimes, 47 percent of burglaries, and 60 percent of assaults involve alcohol.[2] No drug known to man is more widely advertised as sociable, enjoyable, and exhilarating or is more frequently responsible for crimes, injuries, and deaths.

Also revealing is a quick look at suicide. Up to 80 percent of victims have been drinking when they commit suicide. One study found that the suicide rate among alcoholics was thirty times greater than among the general population.[3]

Alcohol robs brains in a variety of ways. As an intern, I saw several men, suffering from alcohol withdrawal, ride into the hospital ward on a pink elephant. At least they thought they were riding one. If it wasn't a pink elephant, the patient would be screaming because he was being charged by a herd of orange buffaloes or clawed by scarlet gorillas. Doctors call this condition delerium tremens, or the DTs, but to the alcoholic it is a living hell.

The large wards of that day became bedlams as the men shouted at and hid from the ferocious animals bent on their destruction.

Once I saw a man try to escape from his imagined attackers by breaking a window in order to leap from the twentieth floor. Fortunately the nurses were quick enough to grasp the tail of his night-gown and pull him back. We had to handcuff those patients to their beds and give them large doses of morphine, but even with our best treatments many of them died.

In 1942, only 48,000 alcoholics were institutionalized. Today, almost 700,000 alcoholics fill up the beds in our mental and general hospitals. This fourteenfold increase is truly startling, because during the last four decades the population has grown only 62 percent. Because chronic alcohol abuse leads to severe brain damage, alcoholism is a leading cause of insanity. Alcoholics are actually committing a slow suicide of their personalities.

The effects of alcohol, however, are certainly not limited to the brain. I remember one of my alcoholic patients who complained that he couldn't raise his hands high enough to shave his beard. Not only does one out of every five alcoholics develop partial paralysis of certain muscles, but many of them complain bitterly about painful nerve inflammation.

Cirrhosis, or hardening of the liver, is a more serious affair because the blood from the gastrointestinal tract is prevented from flowing freely through the hardened liver. As a result of this back pressure on the blood, fluid leaks out of the veins below the liver. The legs become badly swollen and the abdominal cavity becomes so distended with fluid that the victim can scarcely breathe. We can relieve the acute distress of the huge abdomen by inserting a needle through the skin and draining off some of the fluid, and we can slow the fluid accumulation by using new powerful diuretics. But despite modern therapy the fluid often accumulates faster and faster until the patient succumbs.

Because the liver veins are blocked, the blood bypasses the liver by way of the veins of the esophagus. These thinned-out veins balloon and are prone to rupture when food is swallowed or regurgitated. We can give potent drugs to constrict these vessels, place a special balloon in the esophagus to block off the bleeding, or even shunt the blood around the liver with surgical techniques. Yet these patients bring up so much blood, and the bleeding is so hard to control that the death rate approaches 60 percent for each bleeding episode.

The liver is the detoxification center for the whole body. In the liver, most of the body's toxic waste products are broken down to harmless products. Because much of the cirrhosis victim's blood bypasses his hardened liver, many toxins remain in his blood. These toxins poison the brain, resulting in severe brain damage.

Every year, alcohol, the licensed larcenist, steals thousands of lives from our streets and highways, incites thousands of men to murder and suicide, and institutionalizes thousands of others as maniacs and invalids. An amazed Shakespeare exclaimed, "O God! that men should put an enemy in their mouths to steal away their brains. . . ."[4]

Most of these diseases commonly strike people while they are in the prime of life. When a physician witnesses the suffering of people dying at a comparatively young age, he cannot help but wonder why they kill themselves in pursuit of life's so-called pleasures.

I recall a certain New Year's Day. My wife and I arose refreshed and happy; and we thoroughly enjoyed a breakfast of grapefruit, cereal, ham, and eggs. At noon we ate a delectable New Year's dinner with all the luscious trimmings. But not so the other two couples who visited us. They had seen in the New Year with sparkling champagne and had continued drinking until they were thoroughly drunk. They spent the entire morning holding their aching heads, drinking black coffee, swallowing umteen aspirin, and fighting severe nausea. None of the four could eat a bite of the superb feast. As we topped off the meal with a delicious chocolate mousse and looked out across a snow-blanketed field decorated with icicle-covered trees, I had to wonder why intelligent people would suffer such misery just to experience "life's pleasures." Wasn't life much more pleasurable without certain "pleasures"?

Alcohol abuse deprives men and women of the superlatives in life. Enjoyment is blurred or absent in areas of real living—such as recreation, music, art, eating, sex, and conversation. Some people hesitate to walk with Christ because they do not want to give up certain "pleasures." These people need to embrace and experience God's promise, "No good thing will he withhold from them that walk uprightly" (Psalms 84:11 KJV). They need to understand that biblical regulations were written so that man might obtain the greatest amount of joy from life.

It is popularly held that alcohol enables men to reach new heights of sexual performance; but research has shown that large doses of alcohol impair sexual function and that the sex lives of alcoholics are disturbed, defective, and disabled. Large doses of alcohol decrease the body's production of the male sex hormone, testosterone. That is why many impotent alcoholics return to normal sexual function when they discontinue drinking. Shakespeare observed: Drink "provokes the desire, but it takes away the performance."[5]

In recent years, scientists have recognized the effect of a pregnant mother's drinking on the baby she is carrying. When a mother drinks, her baby also drinks; for the alcohol in her blood passes freely into the baby's blood. In this way a baby may become an alcohol addict even before birth. Many a baby's first days in this world are filled with the horrors of alcohol withdrawal. Worse yet, these babies are prone to mental retardation, poor coordination, and abnormal brain waves——the so-called Fetal Alcohol Syndrome. A 1980 study of 12,127 births at one hospital found 203 infants with some form of alcohol-related problem. These complications included spontaneous abortion and smaller-than-normal babies. The researchers concluded that one out of two babies born to alcoholic mothers is damaged before birth in some way.[6]

Alcohol not only robs people of their brains, their health, and their children's health; it also robs their pocketbooks. Money that should provide food, clothes, and proper housing for a man and his family is far too often tossed over the bar. Many families never know anything of the niceties of living, and frequently their deprivations result in serious neglect and unnecessary sickness.

More than 75 percent of America's alcoholics are employed. However, they miss three times as many work days as the average worker. They are likely to become involved in disputes with their coworkers. Yale University professors have shown that the alcoholic's efficiency on the job is only 50 percent.[7] Hence, they aptly refer to the drinker as the "half man." His mind has been compared to a car in a fog. Accident prone, he lacks discrimination and skill. His casualties make up 40 percent of the 12,600 annual work-related deaths and about half of the 2.2 million work-related injuries.

In defense of this massacre, it is argued that our income taxes would be higher if the liquor industry did not exist. One of the arguments for repealing Prohibition was the fact that a renewed alcohol industry would help save the economy from the woes of the Great Depression. Many studies, however, show that without the alcohol industry, society would save billions of dollars. Auto insurance rates could be cut by about 40 percent and health-care insurance by at

---

Economic costs of alcoholism and alcohol abuse in the United States——1975[8]

Lost production	$19.6 billion
Health and medical	12.7 billion
Motor vehicle accidents	5.1 billion
Violent crime	2.9 billion
Social responses	1.9 billion
Fire losses	0.4 billion
Total	$42.6 billion

---

least 12 percent. The preceding table itemizes the economic impact of alcohol abuse in America. A fraction of these billions of dollars would do much for medical research and could save mankind from a wide variety of ills.

Our society could prevent this colossal waste of life and money by following biblical principles. "None of these diseases" is the promise to those who heed the many scriptural injunctions against drunkenness.

Today, however, some experts argue that alcoholism is a disease determined by a person's genes. For example, Dr. Donald Goodwin found that children of alcoholics have an increased rate of alcoholism even if they were adopted by nonalcoholic parents within several weeks of birth.[9]

A person's genes may play a large role; however, a person's actions still determine whether or not he succumbs to this disease. Alcoholism is not inherited like color blindness, for a person's genes do not force him to drink to excess. Blaming a person's genes for alcoholism is like blaming a person's color blindness for running a red light. The propensity to become addicted to alcohol may (at least to some extent) be genetically influenced, but no one believes that intemperance is an inherited trait. A person who never abuses alcohol will never become an alcoholic.

The Bible often warns about the dangers of intemperance with alcohol. As Solomon said: "Wine is a mocker and beer a brawler; whoever is led astray by them is not wise" (Proverbs 20:1 NIV).

A person who follows biblical principles becomes immune to any of the diseases that are caused by alcohol abuse. Here is one passage that warns in crisp but colorful language of the economic, medical, and social ravages of alcohol abuse, even including a description of delerium tremens:

> Listen, my son, and be wise,
>   be guided by good sense:
>   never sit down with tipsy men or among gluttons;
>   the drunkard and the glutton come to poverty, and
>   revelling leaves men in rags.
>
> Who shriek? who groan?
> Who quarrel and grumble?
> Who are bruised for nothing?
> Who have bleary eyes?
> Those who linger over the bottle,
>   those who relish blended wines,
> Then look not on the wine so red
>   that sparkles in the cup;

it glides down smoothly at the first,
but in the end it bites like any snake,
it stings you like an adder.
You will be seeing odd things
you will be saying queer things;
you will be like a man asleep at sea,
asleep in the midst of a storm.

Proverbs 23:19–21, 29–34 MOFFATT

Chapter Four

Coronary and Cancer by the Carton

 The manager of a grocery store phoned me one day. "Doctor," he said, "Mrs. Henderson secretly slipped me a note when I delivered groceries to her house this morning. She says that her husband is very sick—so sick that he is almost out of his head. He won't allow her to leave the house for fear she will never come back. She is afraid he may kill her. She wants you to go to her house to examine her husband."

Mr. Henderson stood over six feet tall. He had been a burly muscular man; but now, his flesh wasted away from his bones and his eyes sunk deep in their sockets, he appeared more like a skeleton than a man. Coughing up masses of blood, he had not slept well for months. His suffering had been long and horrible.

After I questioned and examined him, a diagnosis of cancer of the lung seemed highly probable. By phone I arranged to admit him to the hospital, and it was a big relief to all concerned when the day of his admission arrived. During his first night in the hospital, however, he hemorrhaged severely and drowned, gurgling in his own blood. An autopsy revealed widespread cancer of both lungs.

How often does this sanguinary horror occur in the lives of men and women? In 1983, over 100,000 Americans were strangled to death by lung cancer. The following graph shows that no cancer

AGE-ADJUSTED CANCER DEATH RATES* FOR SELECTED SITES
MALES, UNITED STATES, 1930–1978

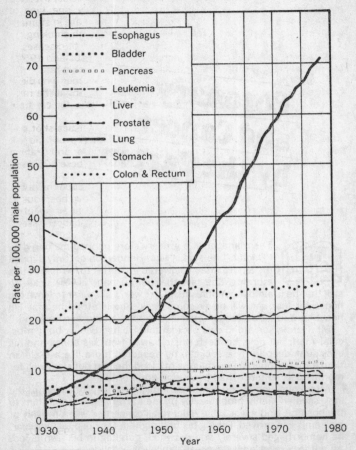

Sources of Data: U.S. National Center for Health Statistics and U.S. Bureau of
the Census.
* Adjusted to the age distribution of the 1970 U.S. Census Population.

FIGURE 1: Age-adjusted death rates from the most common cancers in
American males since 1930.[1]

statistic has ever skyrocketed as high or as rapidly as deaths from lung cancer.

Despite exposure to many new industrial chemicals, Western man has suffered a devastating increase in only one type of cancer—cancer of the lung. The reason for the decrease in stomach cancer is unknown; however, it has nothing to do with smoking.

Back in 1912, lung cancer was called "the rarest of diseases."[2] Then, in the 1920s, it began to increase. In the 1940s and 1950s, the mortality figures zoomed upward at an unbelievable rate.

Today, one out of three men and one out of five women who die of cancer go through the horrors of lung cancer—making it the most common form of cancer in America today. That is a far cry from 1912 when it was the "rarest of diseases."

What is the cause of lung cancer? When the statistics shot skyward, surgeons suspected the cause, but statistical proof did not come until the middle of this century. In 1950 Wynder and Graham reported 605 proven cases of lung cancer. Among these 605 men, only 8 had been nonsmokers.[3]

In the past, cigarette manufacturers have tried to dupe the public into believing that these increases in lung cancer have been due to air pollution. However, recent studies have shown that air pollution is responsible for no more than 5 percent of all lung-cancer cases.[4]

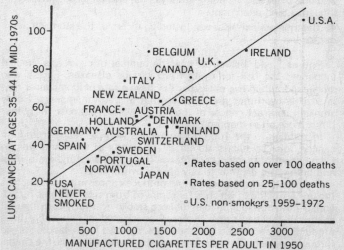

FIGURE 2: International correlation between cigarettes manufactured per adult in 1950 and lung cancer rates in 1970.[5]

The international influence of smoking on lung cancer is shown in figure 2. This graph compares the consumption of cigarettes per adult in 1950 to the rate of lung cancer in 1970 among middle-aged people. Those countries in which cigarette consumption was high when a certain generation was entering adulthood had much higher lung-cancer rates when that generation reached middle age. Those countries that had lower cigarette consumption subsequently had much lower rates of lung cancer.

In 1979, the Surgeon General released a vast summary of all the research to date on the effects of smoking on health.[6] In this immense volume, hundreds of studies of literally hundreds of thousands of people were cited. The results of these studies not only proved that smoking is the major cause of lung cancer, but they also demonstrated that smoking is responsible for many deaths from other cancers and other diseases. The Surgeon General reports that smokers are particularly susceptible to:

1. **Cancers:** including cancers of the lung, larynx, mouth, esophagus, bladder, and pancreas

2. **Cardiovascular Disease:** including coronary heart disease, hypertension, and aortic aneurysms

3. **Lung Diseases:** including emphysema, chronic bronchitis, influenza, and pneumonia

4. **Gastrointestinal Diseases:** including ulcers of the stomach and duodenum.

Figures 3 and 4 illustrate how the number of cigarettes smoked influences the risk for dying from various diseases. People who smoke more than two packs per day have a rate of lung cancer that is seventy-two times greater than that of the nonsmokers! Heavy smokers contract cancer of the larynx (voice box) over thirty-four times more often than nonsmokers.

In addition to the 100,000 Americans who die yearly from lung cancer, tobacco habits slaughter thousands of men and women from cancer of many other organs. The surest way to die a painful and premature death is to buy cancer by the carton.

One wonders how smoking can produce cancer in organs such as the urinary bladder, which is far removed from cigarette smoke. Scientists have now identified in tobacco smoke over forty-two different chemicals that can cause cancer when injected into animals. These products, when inhaled into the lungs, dissolve in the blood, spread throughout the body, and are excreted in the urine. Thus, the chemicals in cigarette smoke contact every organ in the body. The carcinogens and toxins in cigarette smoke include carbon monoxide,

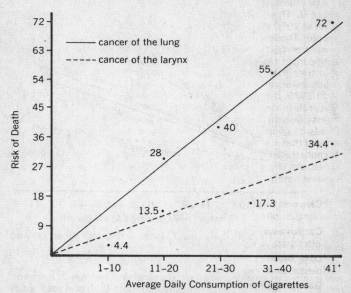

FIGURE 3: Risk for lung and laryngeal cancer death related to amount smoked.[7]

ammonia, cyanide, acetone, benzene, phenol, DDT, methyl alcohol, arsenic, formaldehyde, nitrobenzene, and a radioactive element Polonium–210. From this partial list, you can see that a smoker uses his lungs and body as a veritable toxic-waste dump, rivaling anything created by pesticide companies.

A few years ago I was called out of bed to treat a man who was experiencing severe, crushing chest pain. When I arrived, the man lay on the floor. His face was ashen gray. His eyes stared motionless at the ceiling. He was not breathing; his heart was not beating. He was dead. A clot in his coronary artery had shut off the supply of blood to his heart and had changed his muscular blood pump into a lifeless bag of tissue. The blocked coronary is the master of executioners, killing over 700,000 men and women in America every year.

In my patient's shirt pocket was a partly empty pack of cigarettes. Can smoking cause heart disease? Yes! Looking at figure 4, you can see that the more a man smokes, the more likely he is to die of heart disease. The American Heart Association studied over 7,000 men

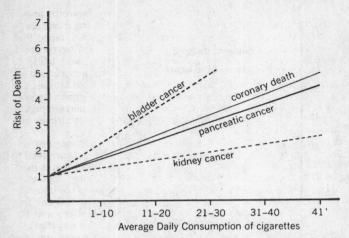

FIGURE 4: Risk for death due to heart attacks and various cancers related to amount smoked.[8]

and found that smoking was indeed associated with death from coronary-artery disease. Those who smoked more than one pack a day
were three times more likely to die from a heart attack than were
their nonsmoking counterparts.[9] About one-third of the 700,000
Americans who die from coronary artery disease are killed by the fire
in their mouths. Thus, in addition to the 100,000 Americans who
yearly succumb to lung cancer, cigarettes kill about 230,000 more
with heart disease.

Not only is smoking the major cause of lung cancer, it is also the
most important preventable cause of fatal heart attacks. Comparing
a cigarette to a coffin nail is far more than a figure of speech.

Cigarettes use several mechanisms to bring about coronary
death. The chemicals in cigarette smoke promote the formation of
atherosclerotic plaques in coronary arteries. Researchers autopsied
over 1,000 veterans and found that heavy smokers were more than
four times as likely to suffer from advanced coronary-artery atherosclerosis.[10] Smoking also increases the stickiness of certain blood
cells; thus, a smoker's blood is more likely to clot within the already-
narrowed coronary arteries.

When the vessel is finally clogged up, the smoker is at a distinct
disadvantage. The nicotine in his blood stimulates his heart to work
harder than normal, so his heart needs more oxygen to support its

higher work load. However, carbon monoxide from cigarette smoke binds very tightly to hemoglobin——the oxygen-carrying molecule—— thereby lowering its capacity to transport oxygen. Thus, blood that gets through or around a clogged artery carries less oxygen to a heart that requires more oxygen due to its increased work load.

Reduction of blood flow and damage to the arteries can cause serious trouble in other organs. In the brain, the damaged arteries are prone to induce clots, thereby causing strokes. The Surgeon General reports that the death rate from strokes is about 70 percent higher in smokers.[11] This percentage is truly startling, since strokes annually strike dead about 120,000 Americans.

Tobacco companies have responded to this vast amount of evidence by producing and heavily advertising "safer" cigarettes. In 1968 these cigarettes made up 2 percent of the United States market; but today, one out of three cigarettes sold is a "safer" cigarette. However, tobacco from these "low nicotine" cigarettes contains the same amount of nicotine as other cigarettes! How can this be? The cigarette manufacturers have developed ventilated filters and porous cigarette papers. These modifications change the way that cigarettes burn, so that the nicotine content measured by the government's machines are falsely low. In fact, studies have shown that the labeled "tar and nicotine" content of cigarettes does not influence the level of nicotine or carbon monoxide in the blood of a smoker.[12]

One study even showed that the risk for heart attacks was the same for those who smoked "low tar" cigarettes and those who smoked "high tar" cigarettes. A person's risk for heart attack was determined by the number, not the type, of cigarettes smoked.[13] Thus, there is no such thing as a "low risk" cigarette.

Emphysema is another common and serious condition caused by smoking. New evidence indicates that emphysema results from several enzyme changes. One enzyme, named *elastase*, circulates in the blood. Elastase breaks down the stretchy lung protein, elastin, that expands all of the tiny air sacs and air tubules in the lung. Fortunately, however, the body makes another molecule, *antitrypsin*, that blocks the breakdown of elastin in the lung. Cigarette smoke destroys the function of antitrypsin; so, the unblocked elastase is free to break down lung tissue. Not only does smoking destroy lung tissue; it also retards repair of the damaged elastin. Cigarette smoke blocks the formation of another enzyme, *lysl oxidase*. Without this enzyme, the body is unable to replace the smoke-damaged elastin. Therefore, cigarette smoke not only causes the body to "digest" its own lungs, but also blocks repair of this damage. Unsupported by elastin, all of the tiny air passages in the lungs collapse; and the smoker slowly suffocates.

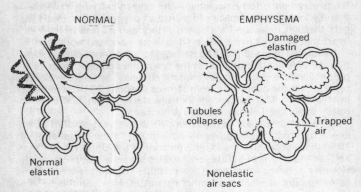

FIGURE 5: Mechanism of suffocation in emphysema.

The Surgeon General reports that the average sixty-three-year-old female smoker has destroyed her lungs to such an extent that they function as poorly as the lungs of the average eighty-year-old non-smoking woman.[14]

One of David's patients had such severe emphysema that he could not even dress himself without becoming breathless. Through a hole in his windpipe, he was connected to a continuous supply of oxygen. Unable to completely exhale through his collapsed airways, his lungs trapped air and blew up like balloons until his chest assumed the shape of a pickle barrel. For the past seven years, he had limited his activity to rolling over in bed, changing the channels on his TV, and smoking his demon cigarettes.

Another effect of smoking is wrinkled skin. One study showed that "crow's feet" were much more common in smokers.[15] One has to question the sanity of a society that spends billions of dollars to get and preserve better looks, yet smokes billions of cigarettes, which irreparably destroy those looks.

Smoking not only decreases sexual appeal, but also decreases sexual fertility. Male smokers are more likely to be infertile. They have decreased sperm count in their semen, and the sperm tend to be abnormal in motility and shape.[16]

Tobacco smoke even affects others in the room. How many times have we all seen a mother cuddle her child while exhaling a cloud of smoke into his face. I have treated many such a child for frequently recurring runny noses, raspy coughs, and sore throats. I have told these parents that their children are so susceptible to these viral infections because their mucous membranes are constantly being irritated by the "second hand" smoke from their parents' cigarettes. Even after my careful explanations, most of them inquired if it would help to try a new medicine for colds, massive doses of some vitamin, or nighttime humidification of bedroom air; yet they seldom asked me how to quit the habit that had caused these colds.

One study showed that after a little over an hour in a smoke-filled room people had inhaled the amount of carbon monoxide equivalent to smoking one cigarette.[17] In addition, at least thirty-nine cancer causing or toxic chemicals have been found in higher concentrations in sidestream smoke (smoke wisping into room air from the lit end) than in the mainstream smoke (smoke inhaled through the cigarette column). Only four such substances have been found in higher concentrations in "mainstream" smoke. Although "sidestream" smoke is diluted by room air, its high concentration of these harmful chemicals partially overcomes this dilutional effect. For example, an extremely potent carcinogen, dimethylnitrosamine, is up to 830 times more concentrated in sidestream smoke.[18]

Has anyone shown that this so-called "passive smoking" actually leads to cancer? Yes, three studies have been published comparing the rates of lung cancer in nonsmoking wives of nonsmoking husbands to the rates of lung cancer in nonsmoking wives of smoking husbands. The combined data from these three studies suggests that nonsmoking women have a rate of lung cancer about 50 percent higher if they are married to men who smoke.[19]

Although tobacco products are heavily taxed at several levels of government, the economic burden of smokers on society is astounding. The following table itemizes the economic costs of smoking in the United States.

Total Economic Costs of Smoking in 1975[20]	
Cancers	$ 4.4 billion
Cardiovascular diseases	12.7 billion
Lung diseases	8.4 billion
Fires	0.4 billion
Cost of tobacco (retail)	15.7 billion
Total cost	$41.6 billion

Although smokers paid $5.6 billion in tobacco taxes, their habit cost themselves and society $41.6 billion—an average of $692 per

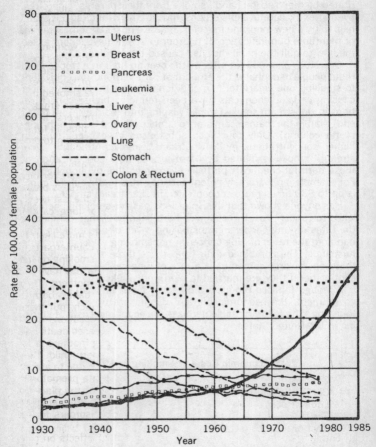

AGE-ADJUSTED CANCER DEATH RATES* FOR SELECTED SITES
FEMALES, UNITED STATES, 1930–1978

Sources of Data: U.S. National Center for Health Statistics and U.S. Bureau of the Census.
* Adjusted to the age distribution of the 1970 U.S. Census Population
Based on projected statistics *Beyond* 1978.

FIGURE 6: Age-adjusted death rate for the most common cancers in females since 1930.[21]

smoker per year. Their excess health costs made up over half of the costs for all lung diseases, about one-third of the costs for all cardio-vascular disease, and about one-quarter of the costs for all cancers. Tell that to a smoker the next time that you hear one claim that his habit supports the economy!

Mention should be made of the effect of smoking on women. The only reason that fewer women are suffering medical tragedies today is that they have not been smoking for as many years as men. In fact, the main reason that women live an average of seven years longer than men is that fewer women than men have smoked over the last several decades. In 1924 only 6 percent of women smoked, but by 1944 about 36 percent of women were smokers. In the 1980s, more teenage girls smoke than teenage boys; thus, in future years, we can expect the life expectancy of women to begin to drop to near that of men.

Figure 6 shows that since 1965 the lung-cancer rate of women has begun to skyrocket just as fast as the lung cancer rate for men did in the 1940s (figure 1). In 1985, lung cancer will surpass breast cancer as the number-one cancer killer of women. In the last twenty years women have more than tripled their rate of lung cancer. Women truly have "come a long way, baby."

Women who take the pill and smoke are five times more likely to die from fatal heart attacks than their nonsmoking counterparts.[22]

Even more frightening is the effect of a mother's smoking on her children. Women who smoke more than one pack per day have two times as many premature babies as nonsmoking mothers. Their babies are, on the average, 6.4 ounces lighter than babies born to nonsmokers.[23] A few ounces may not seem like much, but these lighter babies are much more likely to suffer complications of all types. Thus, infants who are born alive have an increased death rate if their mothers smoked during pregnancy. Smoking mothers, also, more than double their chances of delivering a stillborn child. They are also almost four times as likely to have a stillborn due to abrup-tion of the placenta—a condition where the placenta prematurely tears away from the mother's uterus.[24] Abruption of the placenta often results not only in death of the infant; but also often leads to serious, sometimes lethal, clotting and bleeding disorders in the mother.[25]

Smoking during pregnancy also has long-lasting effects on chil-dren. Researchers studied the children of mothers who smoked dur-ing pregnancy and compared them to children of nonsmokers. This study included almost all 17,000 children born in England, Scot-land, and Wales during a six-day period in 1958. Eleven years later, these children were tested. Children of smoking mothers had lower mental abilities. Even after adjusting for social and biological factors, researchers found that children of smoking mothers had mathematical and reading ages that were an average of about six months behind. These children also had stunted physical growth in that they were an average of 1.5 centimeters shorter.[26]

If one were to tally the excess deaths due to tobacco habits—including those from cancers, strokes, pneumonia, influenza, tuberculosis, emphysema, asthma, ulcers, stillbirths, and coronary heart trouble—the annual total would be about 400,000 Americans.

What should be done about this proven killer? In the early seventeenth century, Turks who were caught smoking were beheaded, hung, and quartered. In Russia under the first czar, smokers had their noses slit, their testicles castrated, their backs flogged, and their bodies exiled to Siberia. Few would endorse such severe methods today, but there are many ways by which our country could reduce tobacco consumption.

Since almost all smokers start before the age of twenty, much effort has been directed at deterring teenagers from beginning this lethal habit. Education and fear, however, have proven to be insufficient motivators; for one study found that even three out of four teen smokers believe that smoking is a bad habit and that it can harm their health.[27]

Why has the widespread knowledge of the dangers of smoking not led to decreased smoking by teenagers? The major obstacle to discouraging smoking is the association of smoking with adulthood and independence. Researchers asked teens to describe two almost identical pictures: one depicted a man with a cigarette in his hand, and the other had the cigarette removed. Teens were more likely to describe the man with the cigarette as adventurous, rugged, daring, energetic, and individualistic. Without the cigarette, the man was more often described as shy, gentle, timid, and awkward.[28] From these studies, we can see that cigarette ads—by associating smoking with rugged, individualistic men and beautiful, sophisticated women—have exerted a tremendous deleterious influence on the impressionable minds of teenagers. Although almost all teens consciously realize that smoking is extremely harmful to their health, cigarette advertisements have successfully sabotaged the onslaught of scientific evidence by attacking at the point where teens are most vulnerable—their subconscious desire to appear grown-up.

Any government that continues to allow smoking advertisement is irresponsible. A survey of Americans found that 62 percent of nonsmokers and 43 percent of smokers felt that cigarette advertising should be banned.[29] The reason that tobacco companies agreed to discontinue television advertisement was a law called the "Fairness Doctrine," which had stated that for every dollar spent on cigarette advertisement, the tobacco companies had to give another

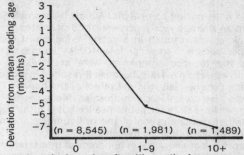

a) Reading Comprehension

(n = 8,545) (n = 1,981) (n = 1,489)

Amount smoked per day after 4th month of pregnancy

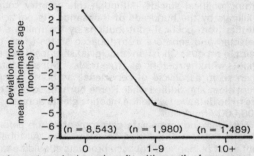

b) Mathematics Ability

(n = 8,543) (n = 1,980) (n = 1,489)

Amount smoked per day after 4th month of pregnancy

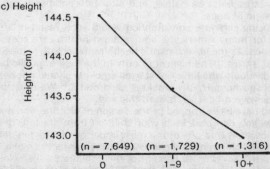

c) Height

(n = 7,649) (n = 1,729) (n = 1,316)

Amount smoked per day after 4th month of pregnancy

FIGURE 7: Intelligence and height of eleven-year-old children related to the smoking habits of their mothers after the fourth month of pregnancy.[30]

dollar to antismoking campaigns. Although prosmoking TV ads resulted in an average yearly increase of 75 cigarettes per person, the antismoking ads resulted in a yearly reduction of over 500 cigarettes per person.[31] In order to get this "Fairness Doctrine" repealed, the tobacco companies were even willing to give up television advertising. Thus, because it resulted in a decrease in antismoking commercials, the net effect of the ban on TV advertisement was an increase in cigarette sales. Many people thought that this ban was a victory for public health, but it turns out that it was just another demonstration of the evil cunning and manipulative power of the giant tobacco industry.

Tobacco is a proven killer of hundreds of thousands of Americans each year, yet the government seems to close its eyes to the evidence. Let us face squarely the reason behind this paradox. Any political party that attacked the $15 billion tobacco industry would be committing political suicide. Although this country counts its tobacco killings by the hundreds of thousands, its politicians count their profits from political contributions by the millions of dollars. Congressmen and senators from tobacco states (even those men who claim to espouse Christian principles) staunchly defend the nicotine giants with the rhetoric of "free trade." Our senators and congressmen seem as devoid of conscience as home computers. As Nero kept aloof and fiddled while Rome burned, so our government appears to be detached while the nicotine giants annually incinerate over 400,000 Americans.

We must demand immediate government action before tobacco habits claim more multitudes of American lives. All tobacco advertisement must be banned. Tobacco products should be taxed to pay for a deluge of antismoking advertisements. Increased production of cigarettes must be halted, and slow but significant reductions must begin at once.

Reducing cigarette consumption would soon result in improved health for many Americans and reduced health-care costs for all Americans. As the government's health representative, the Surgeon General, states, "The highest priority in the field of public health is that individuals who have not started smoking should not begin and that those who currently smoke should quit."[32] We must demand that our government act toward this end.

If you have been trapped by the demon of nicotine, you may wonder how you can best keep your children from starting the habit. Statistics show that one of the most important factors in determining whether children smoke is whether their parents smoke. If both parents smoke, over 20 percent of their children will smoke; but if neither parent smokes, less than 10 percent of their children will become trapped in this filthy habit.[33] Quitting smoking will do more to influence your children's smoking status than anything else you can do. In fact, several studies have shown that parents' *attitudes* toward their children's smoking have no influence on whether their children take up the habit.[34]

Why do people stick their heads into the noose of the smoking habit? A person enjoys the first encounter with smoking in spite (not because) of nicotine, for this drug usually induces nausea and dizziness at the first encounter. Why do they begin? I recall our arrival in Philadelphia from one of our African missionary terms. While we were shopping in the large stores, our three-year-old daughter kept putting little pieces of paper between her lips, and I kept pulling them out. Finally I said, "Linda, why are you putting these pieces of paper between your lips?"

"Daddy, everybody in America has fire in their mouths. This is my fire."

Why do they continue? To many preteenagers and teenagers, smoking is the hallmark of maturity. It is a status symbol to show the world that they have arrived. Smoking soon becomes a "useful accomplishment" to adolescents who are struggling for acceptance and peer status. In difficult situations, instead of fidgeting, they have something to do with their hands. Sharing cigarettes with others gives them a feeling of belonging to a group of friends.

The most important reason, however, that people continue smoking is that they become addicted to nicotine. Nicotine, whether inhaled or injected with a needle, is a habit-producing drug that calls for more and more. Ninety percent of the nicotine in smoke is absorbed into the blood. Within seven seconds it reaches the brain where it is rapidly concentrated. In the brain, nicotine mimics a chemical messenger. First, nicotine stimulates certain neurons by activating nicotine receptors; later, it inhibits these neurons by sticking to their surfaces. Since these neurons are important in portions of the brain responsible for physical and mental arousal, learning, memory, and emotions——it is little wonder that stimulating and inhibiting these centers has a tremendous effect on the nicotine addict. In fact, nicotine is so potent and these neurons are so essential that one drop of pure nicotine placed on the tongue of a dog results in rapid and agonizing death.[35] Serious and sometimes lethal nicotine poisoning occurs when a small child accidentally eats a pack of cigarettes.

The importance of nicotine addiction has been dramatically demonstrated by Dr. M. E. Jarvick. Dr. Jarvick found that monkeys normally preferred to breathe pure air rather than air polluted with cigarette smoke. He forced his monkeys to puff on cigarette smoke, and they soon preferred to breathe air polluted with cigarette smoke. However, when Dr. Jarvick administered a drug that blocked their brain receptors for nicotine, these monkeys again preferred to breathe clean air.[36]

Smokers also continue to require nicotine "fixes" to relieve their anxiety. One researcher found that smokers were able to tolerate high levels of electric shock when they smoked nicotine-enriched cigarettes. Their tolerance to shock, however, decreased when they smoked extremely low nicotine cigarettes.[37] Because of their increased anxiety these nicotine-deprived smokers became unable to tolerate as much aggravation from electric shocks.

The reason that smokers require such frequent "shots" of nicotine is that nicotine is so rapidly broken down and excreted in the urine. In fact, smokers smoke more cigarettes when they are nervous because stress acidifies their urine. Acid urine causes the nicotine to be excreted at a faster rate. Thus, smokers undergoing stress must smoke more cigarettes in order to maintain the same nicotine blood levels.

Another reason that people smoke is simply that it becomes a habit. We are creatures of habit; anything that we repeat daily, hourly, or by the minute—we soon do without thinking. Habits may include tying shoelaces, kissing a spouse, biting nails, or shaking hands. Marcel Proust observed that the strength of a habit is generally in proportion to its absurdity; the absurd habit of inhaling harsh tobacco smoke into delicate lung tissues certainly follows this rule.

I remember a young woman who attended a nearby college where smoking was forbidden. She thought it was sophisticated and smart to sneak a cigarette when no one was looking. She considered the antismoking college standards fanatical and foolish. Because her style was cramped, she finally went elsewhere.

Many years later she called me to see if there was anything that she could possibly do to stop smoking. Something had come up, and she wanted to get rid of her habit. Was there any drug I could send her to deliver her from her bondage. Now she recognized that the maturity she was proud of a few years ago was actually a most disappointing immaturity. The freedom she had sought had slowly enslaved and now constantly tortured her.

Sigmund Freud was a classic example of a slave to nicotine. Smoking twenty cigars a day, he suffered forty years of heart disease and endured thirty-three operations for mouth cancer, from which he eventually died. His doctors strongly warned him that his smoking was probably the cause of his afflictions, yet he found it impossible to quit. On the few occasions that he tried to quit, he suffered the classic symptoms of nicotine withdrawal. Because his brain missed the nicotine-induced, amphetaminelike high, he became depressed and soon returned to his lethal habit. Once, when confronted by a physician, he replied, "I am not following your interdict from smoking; do you think then it is so very lucky to have a long miserable life?"[38]

The benefits of quitting smoking, however, are immense. After only three weeks of abstinence, young adults have decreased heart rates, more efficient breathing, more elastic lungs, and increased exercise tolerance.[39]

Smokers usually find it much easier to quit when they finally get lung cancer or heart disease, but it makes a lot more sense to quit before one gets a fatal disease. Ex-smokers decrease their risks for heart attacks, strokes, and lung cancer. After quitting for five years, smokers more than halve their risk for lung cancer; and after fifteen smokeless years their lung-cancer rate approaches that of non-smokers.[40]

Although gradual withdrawal has been successful for many drug addicts, this technique does not work well for nicotine addicts. People who try to cut down slowly or even just to low-nicotine cigarettes experience all of the symptoms of the smoker who goes "cold turkey," but their discomfort is more severe and more protracted. Dr. Saul Shiffman found that those who quit "cold turkey" had a very rapid decrease in their craving for a cigarette and that their physical symptoms practically disappeared by eight days after quitting. However, those who tried to quit slowly had physical symptoms of discomfort and severe cravings for cigarettes that lasted for the entire two-week study.[41]

I once asked one of my medical colleagues—who, after smoking for most of his life, had quit—if he had found it difficult to stop. "No," he said, "not after I really made up my mind. When I quit, I got rid of the biggest nuisance in my life."

"What do you mean?" I asked. "I thought people smoked because they enjoyed it."

"It's not like that at all," he replied. "I got rid of a grand nuisance. I was always looking for cigarettes, for matches, for ashtrays. I burned holes in my suits and the furniture. When I quit, I got rid of the biggest annoyance anybody can ever have."

He is only one of many thousands of physicians who decided they were fools to continue smoking. Among physicians, a surprising change in attitude has occurred during the past thirty years. Years ago at meetings I had to struggle to see the speaker through a smoky haze. For a day or two afterward I smelled like something smoked. Even the *Journal of the American Medical Association* carried ads for various brands of cigarettes. Today, however, the rare physician who smokes at a medical meeting is considered to be something like a stock market analyst who advises his clients to buy bullish stock but himself buys stock that he knows is going to crash. In David's medical-school class, there were very few students who smoked. Most of those who did smoke tried to hide their habit because their fellow students regarded them with disdain for their lack of self-control. In 1949, about 60 percent of physicians smoked cigarettes. In 1975, a survey of physicians found that only 21 percent of physicians still smoked and 37 percent had quit.[42]

These changes in attitudes and habits have occurred because medical science has discovered and proved that smoking is the greatest single preventable cause of:

Public Killer No. 1—Heart disease
Public Killer No. 2—Cancer

Everybody should be thankful that medical science has opened its eyes to the dangers of smoking. How much more thankful we should be to the Lord because He warned many of His people about and saved countless thousands of His followers from a variety of horrible deaths many years before any scientific studies were done.

I recall the testimony of a man who had been converted in an environment where there was no preaching against smoking. The Spirit of God told him to stop smoking. He thought it very strange for God to make such an odd request of him, but he obeyed. Sometime later he came across passages in the Bible that confirmed the course he had taken.

Tobacco was not used in the Middle East when the Bible was written. It is, therefore, not mentioned specifically in the Bible. The impact of many Bible passages, however, gave sufficient warning to keep millions of Christians from using tobacco in any form even before medical science had proven the dangers of these habits. These admonitions—coupled with observation of tobacco users with their spittoons, smells, smokes, and sicknesses—deterred many believers from indulging.

As early as 1604, King James I of England attacked smoking as, "lothesome to the eye, hatefull to the Nose, harmfull to the braine, dangerous to the Lungs, and in the blacke stinking fume thereof, neerest resembling the horrible Stigian smoke of the pit that is bottomlesse."[43]

In 1653, Jacob Bald, a Jesuit priest, asked, "What difference is there between a smoker and a suicide; except that the one takes longer to kill himself than the other?"[44]

To a Christian, indulgence would be inconsistent with obedience to such Scriptures as:

> Do you not know that your body is a temple of the Holy Spirit, who is in you. . . . You are not your own; you were bought at a price. Therefore honor God with your Body.
>
> 1 Corinthians 6:19, 20 NIV

> If anyone destroys God's temple, God will destroy him; for God's temple is sacred, and you are that temple.
>
> 1 Corinthians 3:17 NIV

> So whether you eat or drink or whatever you do, do it all for the glory of God.
>
> 1 Corinthians 10:31 NIV

Guidance by the Holy Spirit and obedience to the Holy Bible have allowed many Christians to suffer from "none of these diseases"— these diseases caused by tobacco and nicotine.

Chapter Five

They Have the Devil to Pay

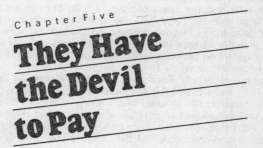

 Click-i-ty, click, click! In Africa when we heard the rapid little clicks of a stick hitting the stony path, we knew it was Saturday, beggar's day. One of the first to arrive was blind Alpha, whose only eyes were on the end of his stick.

Who sinned—this blind beggar or his parents? Probably his parents, since gonorrhea in the mother is the most common cause of lifelong blindness among the people of undeveloped nations. When the mother is infected with gonorrhea, the baby's eyes can become infected as the baby delivers through the birth canal. The delicate coating of the newborn's eye becomes scarred, permanently blinding the baby.

Africa and the East have their multiplied millions of blind beggars, most of them blinded by gonorrhea. Their only food is the crumbs that seldom fall from the tables of an impoverished people. When they ask for bread, they often are pelted with stones, and a pack of lean, mangy dogs often drives them out of town. When night comes, the beggars may carefully feel their way out of the forest to sleep on a porch, which provides only minimal protection against torrential rains and wild jungle animals.

In our country, blind beggars do not clutter the streets; instead, they tap their way around the black corridors of our institutions. Not that many years have passed since about 90 percent of the blind in our institutions were placed there by the gonorrhea bacterium. Today, in countries where silver nitrate for the eyes of newborns is not readily available, colossal indeed is the devastation to eyes, bodies, and lives from this venereal scourge. How tragic it is that hundreds of thousands of hopelessly blind people must pay the devil for the sins of their parents!

Syphilis is also the cause of many a baby born macerated and dead. If an infected baby lives, he may have various physical or mental deficiencies. Not only do these handicapped children have to pay a price during their lives—but their parents, as they look daily on their deformed or insane children, must pay dearly and bitterly with lifelong remorse. In 1946 when penicillin was introduced, a medical text reported: "Each year it is estimated that [in the United States] . . . more than 50,000 infants with congenital syphilis are born."[1] Penicillin has reduced this number to about 100 per year; but in underdeveloped countries—where the World Health Organization estimates that 50 million adults are annually stricken with syphilis—syphilitic infection of the newborn still ravages its many thousands.

Some of these blighted children give birth to offspring whose wretched bodies and minds are also devastated by syphilis. They exemplify the scriptural warning of the visitation of the ". . . iniquity of the fathers upon the children, and upon the children's children, unto the third and to the fourth generation" (Exodus 34:7 KJV). In all, medical science recognizes at least twenty-four different venereal diseases with their many scores of debilitating complications.

I will never forget the first case of blockage of the urinary passage that I saw in Africa. A thirty-four-year-old man gave a history of being unable to pass any urine from the normal passage for many years. The scarring of the passage was caused by a gonorrheal infection from "a lover." Its tubular passage obstructed, the urine had burrowed other little channels around the scrotum. Urine constantly dripped from these openings, and the resulting stench had made him a social outcast. He was indeed a pathetic character. He had found it was a costly business, this paying the devil.

Gonorrhea is not a new disease, and it is likely that the reference to a man with a "bodily discharge" in Leviticus 15 refers to the pusridden penile exudate that usually accompanies a gonorrheal infection. God commanded that the Israelites must declare this man "unclean" and separate him from the people, "whether it [the discharge] continues flowing from his body or is blocked . . ." (Leviticus 15:3 NIV). Knowing that an infected man might also have a gonorrheal throat infection, God specifically mentioned the uncleanness of spit. After his discharge stopped, an infected man remained separate from the people for seven more days. Thus, the Lord made provision for His disobedient people to remain separated while they were most infective to others. Before rejoining his family and after washing and changing clothes, the man had to offer a "sin offering" to "make atonement before the Lord" (*see* Leviticus 15:15).

When penicillin was introduced in the early 1940s, the incidence of gonorrhea and syphilis declined rapidly in Western countries, and many medical experts thought that penicillin would wipe out these venereal diseases. This decrease continued until the 1950s when the trend started upward again. Scientists had underestimated the ability of bacteria to adapt to new drugs; and they also could not have predicted the modern worldwide epidemic of licentious sex. In 1953, a penicillin dose of 200,000 units sufficed for a case of gonorrhea. Today, we must prescribe 5 million units along with another drug, probenecid, which sustains high tissue and blood concentrations of penicillin. The World Health Organization estimates the an-

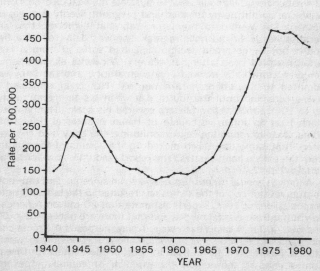

FIGURE 8: Annual rate of American civilian cases of gonorrhea.[2]

nual worldwide gonorrhea incidence to be a phenomenal 250 million people. The failure of penicillin to eradicate gonorrhea in the United States is illustrated in figure 8.

Even more frightening is a new strain of gonorrhea that actually produces an enzyme that breaks down penicillin. This new bacterium seems to be a result of the Vietnam conflict, where after two years of service 50 percent of American soldiers became infected with gonorrhea. Since the GI's and their women often took inadequate doses of penicillin to "protect themselves," the few gonorrhea bacteria that produced the enzyme were able to survive and proliferate. Today, 30 to 40 percent of gonorrhea infections in Southeast Asia are resistant to penicillin. In these countries with limited money for health care, this epidemic may have devastating medical and economic consequences. Because the alternate drugs are much more expensive than penicillin, these countries may not be able to afford to treat gonorrhea, a disease that already makes up a large portion of their infectious-disease cases. Southeast Asia is not a sexual island, and the United States has begun to import an epidemic of penicillin-resistant gonorrhea. Figure 9 shows how rapidly infections of this penicillin-resistant strain have multiplied in the United States.

A patient of David's will serve to illustrate the next disease. Donna K. was a vibrant newly married and pregnant twenty-five-year-old woman. She went into premature labor at eight months; and because her labor did not progress, she was delivered of a five-pound boy by cesarean section. She had suffered from a fever but it resolved soon after her delivery. A careful examination of her premature baby showed only prematurity, and the baby was admitted to the intensive-care nursery. Her child remained in stable condition until the fourth day when his temperature shot up to 104° F. and yellow blisters covered his scalp. The baby was started on an intensive course of the new antiviral drug vibarabine. Despite round-the-clock monitoring, the baby died two days later. That same day David picked up the results of the cultures from the baby's head blisters. The report read, "Positive for herpes simplex type-2."

Although genital herpes has been known since ancient times, the "sexual revolution" of the sixties has resulted in the largest genital-herpes epidemic ever. Experts estimate that 20 million Americans now suffer from genital herpes and that there are between 300,000 and 500,000 new cases each year. Today, herpes is the most common cause of genital sores in women and is second only to syphilis in men. Figure 10 is taken from a report of the Centers for Disease Control, and it shows how the problem of genital herpes has mushroomed in the last decade. This study found that private physi-

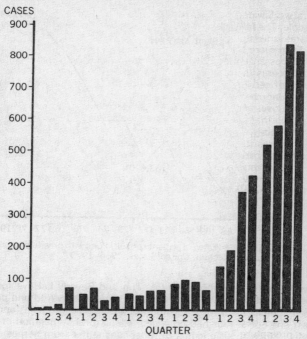

FIGURE 9: Quarterly incidence of penicillinase-producing gonorrhea in U.S. during 1976–1983.[3]

cians saw fewer than 30,000 cases in 1966; but by 1979 they were seeing over 260,000—almost a ninefold increase.

The herpes viruses are divided into two types: type 1, usually causing cold sores ("above the waist")—and type 2, usually causing genital sores ("below the waist"). Twenty years ago only 5 percent of herpes patients had cold sores from type 2 or genital infections from type 1. However, in the intervening years this percentage has climbed to 20 percent. This increase in type 1 genital infections is probably due to the renewed popularity of oral-genital and oral-anal sex. A 1976 survey of 3,377 Christian men and women found that even professed Christians have adopted alter-

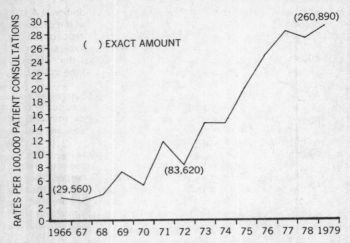

FIGURE 10: Estimated rates of patient consultations with private physicians for genital herpes infection, United States, 1966–1979.[4]

nate forms of sexual intercourse. Tim and Beverly LaHaye found that at least two out of three Christian couples surveyed had practiced cunnilingus (oral stimulation of the female genitalia) and at least one out of four had practiced fellatio (oral stimulation of the penis). Since about one-half of Americans suffer from herpes cold sores, which can be transmitted to the genitals, these practices should be discouraged. Husbands of pregnant women and people with cold sores should absolutely abstain from oral-genital sexual stimulation.

The first attack of herpes begins two to ten days after exposure to the virus. Within several hours, a mild tingling or burning sensation gives rise to painful watery blisters. In women, these blisters often cover large portions of the external genitalia, vagina, and cervix. The infection often results in profuse watery discharge and pain on urination. In men, blisters cluster anywhere on the penis or around the rectum (in homosexuals) and may be confused with syphilitic sores. An acute attack may result in massive and painful swelling of the penis, which makes it difficult and painful to produce a stream of urine. Even after the attack, the passage for urine may be so constricted that doctors must dilate the passage with a series of metal rods.

About 40 percent of people suffering from their first attack actually feel sick with fevers and muscle aches. An additional 4 to 8 percent develop viral meningitis—an inflammation of the coverings of the brain and spinal cord. Most of these patients recover without difficulty, but they must be hospitalized for several days. In most cases no treatment is necessary; and the blisters dry, ulcerate, scab, and heal without scarring. The entire course of the initial bout lasts two to six weeks.

Over half of patients with genital herpes have recurrent attacks, and those with type 2 are about five times more likely to suffer from recurrent attacks. Because the body builds up partial immune defenses to herpes, the symptoms of these recurrences are usually milder and shorter-lived than with the first attack.

As with the unfortunate would-be mother, Donna K., some infected people never suffer noticeably from the disease and are not diagnosed. Many other people, who know they have herpes, shed infective viruses for weeks to months after the symptoms of their infection have disappeared. Thus, there is no way to be sure that any one person with herpes is not infective to others at any given time. One out of two regular sexual partners of an infected individual acquires genital herpes.

Recently, herpes "dating" services have been organized in many large American cities. These organizations promote the idea that "once you have herpes, you don't need to worry about new exposures to the virus." Recent evidence, however, shows that there are hundreds of strains of herpes viruses. A person who is infected with one strain may become infected with another strain and suffer recurrent attacks from both strains. Thus, these herpes sex-pairing services are producing even more misery for the promiscuous herpes victims.

Unfortunately, the herpes virus can survive for several hours on dry objects and up to three days in cloth. Thus, although it is very unlikely, herpes may be acquired from the "infamous" toilet seat; and it is important for people with herpes (genital or oral) to use their own towels and washcloths and keep them separate.

A new drug, acyclovir, decreases the length of the attacks and decreases the number of infective viruses that are shed. However, there is no cure for herpes; and we may have to wait a long time until one is found. A popular saying among college students is, "Love may last for only one night, but herpes is forever."

Sometimes women have to pay a higher price than men. A few decades ago the opening statement of a professor of female diseases to his students was, "Curse the day when a woman walks into your office with pelvic inflammatory disease." He made this statement because of the frightful suffering and lifelong problems that gonorrhea can produce in women. The gonococcus, after producing a pus-ridden vaginal infection, spreads upward through the womb to the tubes, ovaries, and the abdominal cavity. High fever, vomiting, and severe abdominal pain result because of the localized inflammation and abscess formation.

Extensive scarring of the tubes blocks the passage where the sperm and egg must meet; thus, these women may become unable to bear children. After one episode a woman has a 13 percent chance of becoming sterile; after three episodes her risk of sterility soars to 75 percent.[5] The impact of pelvic inflammatory disease (P.I.D.) on the family lives of thousands of Americans can partially be seen in the increase in married women of childbearing age who are unable to bear children. From 1973 to 1976, over 360,000 women became unable to bear children.[6] Experts attribute most of this dramatic increase to the epidemic of P.I.D.

Women who do become pregnant are much more likely to experience ectopic pregnancies—pregnancies where the baby implants in the tubes rather than in the uterus (womb). This is because tubal infection causes scarring, and the scarred tubes provide ineffective propulsion for the fertilized egg. Thus, the egg settles out in a tube and never gets down to the uterus. In 1967 there were 13,200 ectopic pregnancies in the United States; by 1977 this number had skyrocketed to 41,100. Since the tubes are not large enough to hold a baby, they rupture—killing the baby and resulting in a massive loss of the mother's blood. In 1977, ectopic pregnancy was the leading cause of maternal death among nonwhite women in the United States.[7]

In the United States, where there is no shortage of antibiotics, pelvic inflammatory disease strikes about 850,000 women per year—requiring 212,000 hospital admissions, 115,000 surgical operations, and about 2.5 million physician visits. The annual medical cost for treating P.I.D. and its consequences totals over $2.7 billion![8]

In the last few years, scientists have found that other types of bacteria (*Chlamydia, Bacteroides,* and *Mycoplasma*) can also cause P.I.D. Infections with these bacteria tend to be more resistant to antibiotics and are more likely to result in sterility. In some Swedish communities, where the gonococcus has been largely eradicated, the rate of P.I.D. has actually gone up.[9] Thus, eliminating gonorrhea may lead to an overall increase in P.I.D.—a nongonococcal P.I.D. that will cause even more serious problems.

Commenting on P.I.D., noted epidemiologist, Dr. B Frank Polk, states: "In addition to economic costs there are more intangible losses such as guilt and other psychic traumas associated with inability to have children. Disruption of family life, marital discord, and divorce are additional consequences of the sequelae of pelvic inflammatory disease."[10] The devil surely collects his pay when people refuse to heed the biblical warning: "Flee from sexual immorality. All other sins a man commits are outside his body, but he who sins sexually sins against his own body" (1 Corinthians 6:18 NIV).

There is a myth extant that venereal disease can be prevented if intelligence is used. A girl who had sexual relations with only one boyfriend thought she was safe. She was terribly shocked when her doctor told her she was infected. An interview with the boy revealed that he had consorted with only one other girl. But this girl happened to have had relations with five other men, who in turn had been with nineteen women, some of them prostitutes. The girl, who thought her relationship had been limited to a single person, actually had venereally contacted at least ninety-two other men and women.[11]

The limitations of penicillin are particularly conspicuous in its inability to treat some of the worst complications of syphilis. These sometimes develop before the individual is aware that he is infected. This is especially true of women, where the first ulcer of syphilis may be internal and pass unnoticed. The outstanding characteristic of syphilis is its tendency to reawaken to destructive action many years after the original infection. Twenty or more years after the disease is contracted, it may strike down its victim with a dreaded complication.

One complication that was particularly prevalent when I began practicing medicine is called *locomotor ataxia*. Here the nerves of the spine and occasionally the nerves of the head are involved. Disturbances of the head nerves may produce squints, blindness, or deafness. When the spinal cord is affected, the gait is characteristic—the foot is thrown out and then slapped down. Involvement of the nerves to the bladder can cause an inability to hold the urine.

In the light of the following description of locomotor ataxia, one would do well to consider whether the illicit pleasure of a few seconds is worth lifelong misery.

> At the time of sphincteric involvement, sexual debility and eventual impotence are almost invariable. . . . The most horrible of the tabetic symptoms are the crises which may be peripheral or visceral. Agonizing lightning pains occur in the muscles of the extremities, abdomen and chest. They are described by the patient as burning, gnawing, lancinating, twitching, or resembling a stabbing with a hot knife. The attacks come on with the rapidity of lightning; they may last for hours or days with brief intervals of freedom.[12]

Three thousand years ago our heavenly Father sought to save us from such an end:

> My son, attend to wisdom,
>   bend your ear to knowledge . . .
>   that they may save you from the loose woman:
>   her lips drop honied words,
>   her talk is smoother than oil itself,
>   but the end with her is bitter as poison,
>   sharp as a sword with double edge. . . .
> Now listen to me, my son,
>   hold fast to what I say:
>   keep clear of her,
>   never go near her door, lest . . .
>   you are left at last to moan. . . .
> "Ah! why did I hate guidance,
>   why did I despise all warning?"
>   Proverbs 5:1–12 MOFFATT

The Lord not only gives many warnings to help mankind, but Jesus so transforms and fortifies those who know Him with the energy and power of His Holy Spirit that Christians have no acceptable excuse for falling into sexual sin. The Apostle Paul expressed the matter forcibly:

> God's plan is to make you holy, and that entails first of all a clean cut with sexual immorality. Every one of you should learn to control his body, keeping it pure and treating it with respect, and never regarding it as an instrument for self-gratification, as do pagans with no knowledge of God. You cannot break this rule without in some way cheating your fellow-men. And you must remember that God will punish all who do offend in this matter, and we have warned you how we have seen this work out in our experience of life. The calling of God is not to impurity but to the most thorough purity, and anyone who makes light of the matter is not making light of a man's ruling but of God's command. It is not for nothing that the Spirit God gives us is called the *Holy* Spirit.
>   1 Thessalonians 4:3–8 YOUNG CHURCHES

It must be bitter mockery, indeed, for people who steal a little illicit sexual pleasure to end up with sexual impotence, permanent sterility, a dead child, or a broken marriage. Sexual sin often results in sexual punishment.

One of David's medical-school professors hinted at the pathetically helpless view that many modern physicians take toward preventing venereal diseases, when he said, "One of the common characteristics of almost all venereal diseases is that there is no way to prevent them." What he meant was that medical doctors have no vaccines or other easy measures for prevention, but his statement still underscores the inability of modern medicine to cope with this immense problem. Many modern students of venereal diseases tauntingly state that it is not immorality that causes gonorrhea; rather, it is the gonorrhea bacterium that causes the disease. That is like saying that Lee Harvey Oswald did not shoot John F. Kennedy; rather, a high-powered rifle shot the President. Following this line of reasoning, however, humanistic physicians have futilely attempted to control the problem solely with "miracle" drugs and expensive research. They reject the moral principles of the Bible as "archaic"—even though biblical principles are the only effective health measures for controlling venereal diseases.

In an effort to seem tolerant, the majority of doctors have taken a position of moral indifference toward their patients. The only reason they give for abstaining from sexual activity is the danger of venereal diseases or unwanted pregnancies. As far back as 1924, however, the Commission of Christian Social Morality recognized the insufficiency of fear as a deterrent for sexual promiscuity; for they wrote: "What is needed is not a mere unwillingness to perform the act, but a moral repudiation of it. . . . To be satisfied with saying 'Avoid this, or you will suffer from it' is to stimulate ingenuity to find a means by which the consequences can be avoided."[13]

Prophetic words, indeed!

In spite of penicillin, in spite of venereal-disease clinics, and in spite of educational programs—the United States Public Health Service reports that in 1977 there were 2 million new cases of gonorrhea. If we have these figures in the United States, where doctors can treat with a host of antibiotics, it is staggering to imagine the predicament of the great bulk of the world's population—many of whom are deprived of medical care, information, and antibiotics.

Yet long before man knew the cause of the affliction or the method of the transmission of venereal diseases, God knew all about them and gave to man the only feasible plan for preventing these universal killers. God clearly stated that sex was intended to be enjoyed only within the confines of marriage (see Exodus 20:14). Even the common ancient Middle Eastern practice of prostitution in places of worship was absolutely forbidden to the Israelites (see Deuteronomy 23:17). This plan of two, and two alone, is so different from human inclinations and so effective in the prevention of the vast complications of horrible venereal diseases, that again we must recognize another medical evidence that an all-knowing and caring God guided the hands of the men who penned the words of Scripture.

Chapter Six

The Superlatives in Sex

 "Doctor, I can't sleep; I can't enjoy anything any more. . . . It all started when Gil began to play cards with the guys. They don't gamble, but they go out every Wednesday night to an expensive hotel for a big steak dinner. Then they play cards until one or two in the morning. Everything's on the up and up, but——"

Pretty Mrs. Gilbert Steiner swallowed and continued. "Oh, I know I'm being foolish. But still, here's the way I look at it. With our five children, we have to watch every penny. I've told Gil that I get bored and nervous staying home month in, month out. I've asked him to take me out to the movies or to dinner once in a while, but he always says there is no money for that and a babysitter, too. He takes the little money we could use for recreation and spends it on himself. Gil resents my attitude. He says that he works hard for his money, so he should be able to decide how it's spent. With all this tension, we aren't enjoying each other at all."

Here was a marriage falling apart because an important cohesive had been lost. The password to a happy marriage is *together*—think together, pray together, plan together, work together, play together, and love together. Two people cannot be held together long unless there is some sort of binding force; and sex is a short-lived binder, as the sex marriages of Hollywood have long demonstrated. Because sex is the only cohesive that many couples know anything about, it comes as no surprise that one out of every two marriages ends in divorce.

One binder, however, has never failed to hold two people together—*love*. "Love never fails." Is this love the "puppy love" played up in novels and on TV? Is this love the love of which the Beatles sang, "All We Need Is Love"? What kind of love is this love—this love that is the essence of every happy marriage?

Although most people understand the meaning of sexual love, few have a clear concept of love in its totality. The vagueness concerning love is evidenced by the eight different definitions given by my dictionary.

C. S. Lewis divided the loves of human relationships into four types: affection, friendship, sexuality, and Charity. Although all of these loves are necessary, they can only be properly fulfilled when they grow out of Charity. Charity can only be obtained as a gift from God, and "it desires what is simply best for the beloved."[1] Charity in a man "enables him to love what is not naturally lovable."[2]

C. S. Lewis argued that Charity is an essential cohesive in any human relationship because, in our fallen state:

> There is something in each of us that cannot be naturally loved. It is no one's fault if they do not so love it. . . . You might as well ask people to like the taste of rotten bread or the sound of a mechanical drill. . . . All who have good parents, wives, husbands, or children may be sure that some times—and perhaps at all times in respect of some one particular trait or habit—they are receiving Charity. [They] are loved not because they are lovable but because Love Himself is in those who love them.[3]

In this chapter, I wish to discuss only those types of love that are turned into Charity: those loves that involve an outward reach of the mind to help and please the beloved.

Charity in itself is not sexual, but only through Charity can we experience the superlatives of sexual love. The superlatives in sex—the best quality, the most enjoyment, and the longest duration—are only possible when coexisting with sexual desire are thoughtfulness, consideration, tolerance, and forgiveness.

Mr. Guy Bullom is continents away from the superlatives when he blatantly asserts that he is going "to look after No. 1," both in his business and his sex life. He constantly berates his wife for her faults, yet he cannot understand why she lacks enthusiasm for his approaches. Although he has had several "affairs" with his secretaries, he fails to realize why none of them satisfied him. Frequency and variety are empty substitutes for stability and quality, and Mr. Bullom knows nothing of that superlative—the best.

This oversexed, self-centered individual gets practically nothing out of sex for the simple reason that he puts practically nothing, besides physical exertion, into it. His love life is unfulfilling because he lacks Charity. As a result he is always disappointed and frustrated sexually. The enjoyment and intimacy of a few minutes are quickly supplanted by an intolerable awareness of the loneliness and sadness that he is trying to escape.

Dr. Carl Jung recognized the underlying reason why many a man like Guy Bullom must endure such an unhappy existence: "It arises from his having no love, but only sexuality . . . and no understanding, because he has failed to read the meaning of his own existence."[4]

There are countless unhappy marriages, devoid of sexual fulfillment, because the couples do not know that without Charity sexuality is empty. The only love they know is something pictured in torrid magazines, filthy novels, romantic movies, and popular songs.

Yvonne had never heard that any other type of love existed. She put her head on my desk and sobbed. After a while she blurted out, "I was only kidding when I said something about Mike's mom. But he got angry and said something awful about my mother. Then I slapped him good and hard across his face—just what he deserved! But the big brute up and punched me in the eye. Look at my eye! I'm moving out! I'm taking the kids and going back to Mom's. I love Mike, but I can't take this!"

While Yvonne held an ice bag over her left eye and looked at me with the other, I gave her a little marriage counseling—somewhat belated for sure. I ended my lecture with words something like these: "Yvonne, in every marriage, situations are bound to arise in which one of the partners must give in, out of consideration and love for the other partner. Don't feel sorry for yourself if you feel that you are the one who has to give in most of the time. I have strange but good news for you: when you give in to Mike, you are losing your life in the only way to find worthwhile happiness. The secret of happiness in married life depends on both partners making small sacrifices, readily and cheerfully.

"You say you have love for Mike. Is it the kind of love that 'suffers long and is kind'? The only love that will stand the acid test of everyday living is that love which God describes and gives to those who live according to His will: 'Love is patient; love is kind and envies no one. Love is never boastful, nor conceited, nor rude; never selfish, not quick to take offence. Love keeps no score of wrongs. . . . There is nothing love cannot face; there is no limit to its faith, its hope, and its endurance. Love will never come to an end.' '' (1 Corinthians 13:4–6;7,8 NEB.)

Millions of couples are not happy. They have extramarital affairs, but their frustrations only increase. They wrangle during the day, so sex becomes lifeless and mechanical—if not repulsive. The feelings they long for can only be obtained when Charity for each other exists. They can never experience real and lasting ecstasy unless the sex act is the consummation of a relationship infused with Charity—an intense awareness of the needs and desires of the other.

Frustrated couples often think there must be something wrong with their "sex departments," so they go off to a psychiatrist for help. Fortunate they are if they go to one who understands the principles outlined by psychoanalyst Erich Fromm:

> The injunction, "Love thy neighbor as thyself," is the most important norm of living and . . . its violation is the basic cause of unhappiness and mental illness. . . . Whatever complaints the . . . patient may have, whatever symptoms he may present, are rooted in his inability to love—if we mean by love a capacity for the experience of concern, responsibility, respect and understanding of another person and an intense desire for that other person's growth. Analytic therapy is essentially an attempt to help the patient gain or regain his capacity for love. If this aim is not fulfilled, nothing but surface changes can be accomplished.[5]

Charity is as essential to happiness and mental health as is food to our strength and physical health. Men, particularly, often fail to comprehend that sex alone is inadequate nourishment for a happy marriage. Sexual climax in men is often a purely mechanical act, while in women it is much more complex. A woman must be fully aware of the man's thoughtfulness for her, of his fidelity to her, and of his desire to put her pleasure ahead of his own.

Psychiatrist Max Levin recognized that unselfish love is necessary for obtaining the superlatives in sex:

> It is obvious, then, that maturity is a prerequisite for a happy marriage. In the immature state of infancy there is no obligation to give. The infant receives; he is not expected to do anything else. The success of a marriage will depend in great degree on the extent to which the partners have outgrown their infantile dependency and

achieved the capacity to assume responsibility, to wish more to give than to receive.[6]

Centuries before Yvonne and Mike had their childish quarrel and centuries before the birth of modern psychiatry, the Bible showed the necessity of maturity in love—a splendid prescription for a happy marriage: "When I was a child, my speech, my outlook, and my thoughts were all childish. When I grew up, I had finished with childish things. . . . In a word, there are three things that last forever: faith, hope, and love; but the greatest of them all is love" (1 Corinthians 13:11,13 NEB).

Loveless and selfish sex forces people to daydream just to escape their reality—a horrible nightmare; but thoughtful and unselfish love allows couples to experience what most merely dream of.

One of many who discovered this truth the hard way was the prodigal son.[7] His was the voice of immaturity: "Give me." He, like many today, hastened into a country far removed from his father's values and there wasted his endowments of money and body "with riotous living." His wild scramble after self-gratification left him unhappy and penniless. He hit bottom in one of life's hogpens where he yearned to eat the empty husks that the pigs were crunching. He discovered that sex removed from God's will is empty, disappointing, and ugly. Self-gratification is ever a one-way street—with a hogpen at the end.

Remembering that his father's house always had "bread enough and to spare," he realized that his father's "horrible religious inhibitions" were not as bad as he had once believed. He began to comprehend the close relationship between proper inhibitions and abundant blessings.

When he had left home, his immaturity was evidenced by his attitude of "Give me." When he returned, the spirit of "Give me" was absent. In its place was a penitent thoughtfulness for others— "Make me a servant."

The emptiness of many marriages is underscored by the fact that most women never experience sexual release during intercourse. Ronald M. Deutsch comments on this problem:

> It appears that by the end of the first year of marriage, perhaps a little more than a third of women have rather dependable orgasm. By the tenth year of marriage, this percentage increases to no more than perhaps 40 percent. . . . No more than 15 percent of American women can depend upon a fully satisfying sex life.
>
> [In one large survey, however,] of those women who

said they never had orgasm, or did so only rarely, fully
half reported enjoying relations either "much" or "very
much."

Of the women who said they had "some" orgasms,
fully two-thirds reported "much" or "very much" enjoyment.[8]

Although millions of preorgasmic women do not feel cheated of
sexual pleasure, these "satisfied" women simply do not know what
they are missing. Orgasms in women can be just as (and often,
more) exciting for women as they are for men, and almost all of
these preorgasmic women are physically able to reach sexual climax. One Christian marriage counselor, Dr. Herbert J. Miles, reported that of 151 young couples to whom he had given thorough
premarital counseling, 96.1 percent of the wives experienced
"definite orgasm during marital intercourse."[9] Thus, with a little information, a few muscle exercises, and a cooperative husband—almost all women can experience the thrill of single or even multiple
orgasms.

Every Christian married husband and wife should read an accurate, up-to-date, and sensitive book on sexual intercourse. Most of
this information could be gained by caring and open communication
between a husband and wife. But when it comes to the bare details,
it is a rare couple that is able to honestly, intelligently, and dispas-
sionately discuss this subject. Two excellent books that sensitively
deal with this subject from a Christian perspective are The Act of
Marriage by Tim and Beverly LaHaye[10] and Intended for Pleasure by
·Ed and Gaye Wheat.[11] Any Christian man or woman who wants to
get more out of sexual intercourse should read one of these books.

Ronald M. Deutsch comments on the need for sex education even
among those who have been married for considerable periods of
time:

> Though science has learned much about the physical
> side of sex in the last two decades, little of this knowledge
> has been communicated. As sex researcher Dr. William
> Masters wrote recently in the Journal of the American
> Medical Association. . . .
> "With any marital unit, one can anticipate that the
> couple has a vast amount of misinformation, misconcep-
> tion, and quite simply, inadequate knowledge of sexual
> physiology."
> This may seem curious in a time when we are so open
> about sex, when the subject is so frankly overworked and
> coldly exploited by commerce of every kind. Oddly, it

seems to be only the useful and accurate information which is excluded from the torrent of sexual dialogue.[12]

The LaHayes comment: "A few years ago, sexual ignorance was a reasonably acceptable excuse for orgasmic incapability, but that day is past. Regrettably some husbands are carryovers from the Dark Ages, like the one who told his frustrated wife, 'nice girls aren't supposed to climax.' Today's wife knows better."[13]

The Wheats add:

Applying the information given in this book [*Intended for Pleasure*], today's husband has the opportunity to become a skillful lover—one who can tenderly lead his wife into the richest pleasures of the sexual relationship—and remember: Every wife should be given the opportunity to experience sexual release in every intercourse. The relationship may be very loving and warm, but this is not enough. Fulfillment ahead! This can be yours![14]

Only the husband who puts the pleasure of his wife ahead of his own pleasure can experience the feelings of joy and virility that come from being married to a thoroughly and titillatingly satisfied woman. Thus, only through that love called *Charity* can a couple achieve mutual sexual ecstasy.

Someone has said: "The cure of all the ills and wrongs, the cares, the sorrows and the crimes of humanity—all lie in one word, 'love.' It is the divine vitality that everywhere produces and restores life."

How can we obtain and maintain this *summum bonum*? We can only obtain love in its fullest measure when we allow God, the Giver of Charity, to dwell within and control without. Nothing less than the divine indwelling will suffice when we find ourselves in the strong current of sexual temptation. We can maintain this love by obediently following the leadings of the Word and the Spirit. There is no acceptable excuse for the Christian to become enmeshed in the web of sexual sin—inevitably resulting in a host of physical, psychological, and spiritual venereal diseases. For the promise of God is sure: "No temptation has seized you except what is common to man. And God is faithful; he will not let you be tempted beyond what you can bear. But when you are tempted, he will also provide a way out so that you can stand up under it" (1 Corinthians 10:13 NIV).

This faithful God not only empowers men and women to triumph over temptation; but, as we have seen, He also infuses couples who wish for a satisfying and fulfilling relationship with the essential selfless love—Charity.

Chapter Seven

The Alternatives in Sex

 "I've always felt I had a charmed life. . . . Things always seemed to work out for me. I feel I've been able to make the best of whatever life has delivered. I'm somewhat of a putterer and a fixer. I change what I can and try not to worry too much about everything else. I'm dealing with my illness the same way I've dealt with everything else in my life. I know that unless the medical profession comes up with something, I'm going to die. But I'm not afraid of death. I've lived a very full life and I don't regret a single thing."[1] These are the words of a California psychiatrist who was living with a deadly illness.

In the mid-1970s, several years after graduating from medical school, Dr. Riley started a practice in San Francisco. "Things really came together for me when I moved to California. . . . I was ready to settle down into a permanent relationship. Mike and I have had a very happy, stable relationship and we've enjoyed many, many wonderful times in the house."[2]

The couple started up a frame shop together, and they led a fairly uneventful life until 1981 when Dr. Riley went on a ten-day all-homosexual "dream trip" Caribbean cruise. After returning, however, Dr. Riley was stricken with anal herpes. For the next year, the three- to four-week attacks recurred with only a week to ten-days respite between episodes. In December of 1982, Dr. Riley's scalp became plastered with the painful blisters of shingles, which felt as though someone was sticking him "with pins and needles 24 hours a day."[3]

Purple cancerous tumors of Kaposi's sarcoma covering the roof of his mouth settled the diagnosis: George Riley, M.D., suffered from acquired immunodeficiency syndrome or AIDS! In April a simple viral infection made him so sick that he became depressed and later said, "If someone had taken me to a bridge, I would have jumped, had I been strong enough to get up."[4] His enjoyable all-gay "dream trip" to the Caribbean Sea had turned into an uncontrollable all-suffering nightmare plunge into the River Styx.

What is this horrible disease? Early evidence showed that AIDS was a disease in which the immune defenses of the body failed, and normally harmless germs could then ravage the victim's body. Several cancers were also found in AIDS victims: cancer of the rectum, cancer of the tongue, and Kaposi's sarcoma.

Since the disease usually takes months to years to squeeze the life out of its victims, only 40 percent of all patients have already died. However, most experts feel that—barring the discovery of some miracle drug—almost all AIDS victims will die within several years after contracting the disease.

In early 1982, only 159 cases of AIDS had been reported; and only one of these patients was a woman. Over 92 percent of these early cases were in men with definite histories of homosexual encounters. Today, however, the disease is attacking other segments of the population. Scientists worry that it may soon become a fairly common venereal disease and may, in the future, become a significant risk to those patients who need life-saving blood transfusions.

By August 8, 1983, doctors had reported 2008 cases of AIDS to the Centers for Disease Control. Homosexuals made up 1429 (71 percent) of these cases. The first homosexuals afflicted with AIDS were particularly promiscuous, averaging over 1,200 sexual partners each. In July of 1982, three cases of AIDS were reported in hemophiliacs who had received clotting proteins pooled from the blood of thousands of donors. This transmission of the disease suggested that AIDS was an infectious disease. Further evidence came from the report of a case in a woman who was a sexual partner of a man with AIDS. Soon doctors documented clusters of AIDS cases among homosexual men and their sexual partners. All this evidence pointed to an infectious agent that could be transmitted through blood products or sexual contact.

AIDS has rapidly spread throughout the United States and has been reported in twenty other countries. In July of 1982, doctors reported 49 new cases of AIDS; during July of 1983, the number of new cases mushroomed to a frightening 235. Figure 11 shows just how rapidly the disease continues to spread.

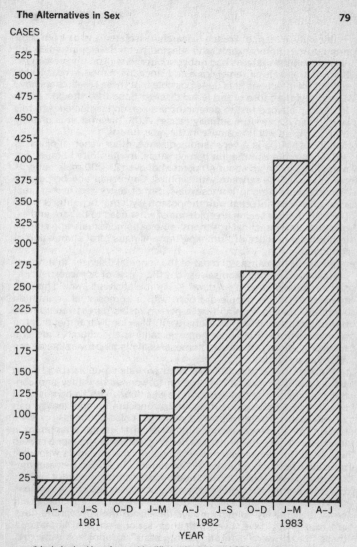

* Includes backlog of cases identified at beginning of CDC surveillance

FIGURE 11: Cases of AIDS by quarter of the year in the United States.[5]

Recently, a team of French researchers isolated a virus from eight promiscuous homosexuals who seemed to be developing AIDS but whose immune systems had not yet undergone disastrous changes. Since this virus is extremely rare and since these men were still able to fight off infections, it is quite possible that these researchers have discovered the cause of this lethal disease. Soon they should be able to develop a blood test to determine if a person is infected with this virus. Even if this virus actually causes AIDS, however, it is unlikely that scientists will find a cure in the near future.

Although AIDS is a very serious disease, other venereal diseases are much more common in homosexuals. In the United States, homosexuals make up about 40 percent of over 27,000 male patients per year who are stricken with syphilis. Gonorrhea and herpes are also common among homosexuals. Six of every ten homosexual men have been infected with the potentially lethal hepatitis B virus. Doctors are now seeing an epidemic of what used to be rare and exotic protozoal intestinal infections, among homosexuals who engage in the filthy practice of "rimming" or anilingus (oral stimulation of the anus).

We know the causes of most of the venereal diseases that homosexuals pass among themselves, but the cause of homosexuality itself has been harder to pin down. "Gay liberationists" would have us believe that some people are born with a homosexual orientation and that there is nothing that a person or his parents could have done before or can do now to change it. They loudly trumpet that the only thing unnatural about homosexuality is the church's attitude toward it and that their own homosexuality is as irreversible as the church's attitude.

Because these "facts" have been so widely popularized by the press, many Christians have begun to wonder how they can condemn a person's sexual actions if he was "born with" a homosexual orientation. Furthermore, if we are to condemn homosexuality, can we not also condemn Down's syndrome, color blindness, or even black skin? Evidence abounds, however, that sexual orientation is learned and not inherited; it has nothing to do with whether a person was born male or female. For example, in the past girls who were born with genitals that looked somewhat male were sometimes raised as boys. These "boys" would gladly undergo painful surgery to remove breasts or make other physical changes consistent with their mistaken sexual identity. Genetically girls but psychologically boys, these "boys" almost always developed the appropriate "heterosexual" sex drive. Even with their serious physical limitations, these "boys" were determined to pursue relationships with girls, whom they perceived to be the opposite sex.

One Saturday, I was in the front yard mowing the lawn when a station wagon pulled into the driveway. Out of the driver's seat stepped Mrs. Jackson. I heard her say to her husband in her drill-sergeant tone, "Hurry up, Marvin. We don't have all day." Leaving him behind, she came storming across the yard. I turned off the mower so that I could hear her better, but I wouldn't have had any trouble even with the engine roaring.

"Doctor Mac," she bellowed, "you've got to help me. My baby, Danny Boy, has decided that he's gay; and he's going to move in with another man. He's always been such a wonderful boy; he's never done anything wicked like this before."

"Doc," Mr. Jackson added while Mrs. Jackson caught her breath, "it's his life, but we were just wondering—"

"Aw, shut up, Marvin. You hardly even know my Danny Boy. It's all your fault."

The Jacksons wanted my help, but they had come too late; for most evidence shows that the family has a tremendous influence on sexual preference only during the early years of life. However, Dan was now eighteen, so changes in his parents' attitudes would proba-bly have little effect now.

The Jacksons' family life story is repeated thousands of times over. The home environment in which children grow up often deter-mines their sexual orientation, and Dan's home environment was classic for the development of a homosexual orientation. Many stud-ies have consistently found certain family patterns in the back-grounds of homosexual men. As did Dan, most homosexual men have close-binding mothers who dominate and belittle their hus-bands. A full two-thirds of homosexual men, but only one-third of heterosexual men, report "close-binding, intimate" relationships with their mothers.[6] Certain orders of birth predispose a boy toward this type of relationship with his mother, and one study found that out of 127 homosexual men, 102 were only sons or youngest sons.[7] Many complain that their mothers babied and restricted them by discouraging sports with other boys, preventing dates with girls, and forcing them into "feminine" household activities. As did Mrs. Jackson, about 60 percent of these mothers openly prefer their sons to their husbands and try to get their sons to take sides against their fathers.

As have many mothers of homosexual men, Dan's mother had even slept in the same bed with her only son, "Danny Boy," until he was thirteen years old, when his friends found out and began to tease him mercilessly. Such an intimate and inappropriate relation-ship with his mother caused conflict in Dan's subconscious mind. His mother "loved" him more than she even loved her husband, and this made him feel guilty for causing marital discord. Thus, he became afraid of his relationship with his mother and later generalized this fear to a relationship with any woman.

One factor that seems to influence whether a boy will generalize this fear to all women is the absence of sisters in the home. On the average, homosexual men have fewer sisters than heterosexual men.[8] Sisters probably help to allow a boy who has an abnormally close relationship with his mother to develop more normal relationships with other females while he is still young.

One interesting experiment demonstrated how this fear of intimacy with his mother influences the sexual preference of the homosexual. In front of homosexual and heterosexual men, researchers very rapidly flashed vulgar words referring to sexual relations with their mothers. Although the men were not conscious of these words, they perceived them in their subconscious minds. After viewing these words, homosexuals, but not heterosexuals, showed an increased appetite for viewing pictures of other men. This experiment indicated that at least part of a homosexual's flight from intimacy with women stems from his excessive fear of intimate contact with his mother.[9]

Not only do the mothers of homosexual men share certain traits, their fathers also share certain characteristics. Eighty-four percent of homosexuals, but only 18 percent of heterosexuals, reported that their fathers were indifferent or uninvolved during childhood.[10] Dan's father was a cross-country truck driver, who spent most of his free time at a bar with his buddies and who had little time for his "sissy" son. Another study also found that over 80 percent of the fathers of homosexual men were either absent or spent very little time with their sons. Most of these homosexuals both hated and feared their fathers. The authors concluded that a warm, supportive, and masculine father practically ruled out the development of homosexuality in a boy.[11]

Dan lacked a proper male role model so he took on his mother's interests, including cooking, sewing, bubble baths. One study found that 67 percent of homosexuals reported "sissy" tendencies during childhood, but only 3 percent of heterosexual men reported these tendencies.[12]

Mrs. Jackson often referred to sex as dirty and repulsive. She had taught Dan such extreme prohibitions against sexual intimacy that he had repressed all heterosexual inclinations as bad or sinful. If he met a girl whom he found attractive, he panicked when his repressed heterosexual desires threatened to emerge. Thus, his homosexual desires seemed to develop out of a frantic flight from women. These attitudes naturally arose from a childhood where relationships with girls were prohibited and intimacy with his mother was required.

One study found that an amazing three-quarters of the mothers of homosexual men had a "puritanical" or frigid attitude toward sex.[13] These mothers had irrational and inconsistent attitudes in that they were afraid to answer questions about sex and would not let another child see their son on the toilet. However, these mothers tended to have little objection to "little white sins," such as not returning a borrowed coin.[14]

D. J. West comments, "The most important factor in bringing about a successful adjustment is a favourable interaction between parents and child during the critical phases of development. . . . A fearsomely repressive, puritanical upbringing risks producing a sexually inhibited adult liable to resort to all kinds of deviant substitutes for straightforward heterosexual intercourse."[15]

He also recognizes that certain prohibitions are also necessary for proper sexual adjustment. To this effect he states, "In their natural, unrestrained state children appear to be totally undiscriminating . . . in their sexual inclinations. Without repression, we might all become anally and orally erotic, sadistic, incestuous and bisexual."[16]

In light of all this scientific evidence demonstrating the influence of family relationships on the development of homosexuality, let us look at what the Bible describes as proper family relationships—relationships that would have prevented Dan's aberrant sexual preference. Paul states, "Wives, submit to your husbands as to the Lord" (Ephesians 5:22 NIV). Such a wife would not have become a close-binding mother who dominated her husband. She would not have belittled her husband's importance, nor would she have tried to get her son to take sides against his father.

The biblical role of the father is also enlightening. Paul states, "Fathers, do not exasperate your children; instead, bring them up in the training and instruction of the Lord" (Ephesians 6:4 NIV). Such a father would not have been distant or uninvolved in the upbringing of his children. Neither would he have been hostile toward his son, who later rebelled. What a complimentary testimony is that of Solomon, who spoke of his father, David, "When I was a boy in my father's house, still tender, and an only child of my mother, he taught me and said, 'Lay hold of my words with all your heart; keep my commands and you will live' " (Proverbs 4:3,4 NIV).

Psychiatrists have often blamed the "puritanical" attitude of mothers of homosexuals on "religious taboos on sexuality." What a surprise would be in store for these psychiatrists (and also these mothers) if they were to read the biblical poetry of Solomon:

How beautiful you are and how pleasing,
  O love, with your delights!

Your stature is like that of the palm,
  and your breasts like clusters of fruit.
I said, "I will climb the palm tree;
  I will take hold of its fruit."
May your breasts be like the clusters of the vine,
  the fragrance of your breath like apples,
  and your mouth like the best wine.
                                         Song of Songs 7:6–9 NIV

The Bible does not take a frigid or "puritanical" view of sex. Rather, the Bible takes that potentially overwhelming river of sexuality and properly channels it into the tranquil and luscious valley of marriage. In the context of marriage, sex is seen as neither taboo nor dirty; but as a beautiful, yet earthly, expression of Christ's love for the Church.

Contrasting with biblical teachings on sexuality are the life-styles of homosexuals. Rather than call their life-styles deviant, promiscuous, lonely, or selfish, they use such euphemisms as "normal, enjoyable, gay, or alternate." The casual and unattached attitudes that characterize male homosexuals can be best demonstrated by some statistics gathered in the San Francisco Bay area during the pre-AIDS era. Sixty-six percent of homosexuals surveyed had "cruised" (picked up sexual partners) in bars during the previous year, 54 percent had "cruised" in public baths, and 48 percent had "cruised" on the street. Although half were currently involved in an "affair," only 8 percent were involved in their first affair; and a similar percentage had been involved in their current "affair" for over five years. Three-quarters of those surveyed had not felt even "some affection" for over half of their partners.[17]

D. J. West observes:

Homosexuals themselves have to admit some truth in the play *The Boys in the Band*, which depicts gay life as "replete with jealousy, competitiveness, insecurity, malice, tantrums and hysterical mood shifts." The obsessive preoccupation with sexual topics wherever gay circles foregather gives the impression "that homosexuals are devoted to full-time sexual musical chairs." The romantic newcomer searching for a permanent love-match is in for a disappointment. Few love affairs between males are lasting. All too often they degenerate into boredom or jealous quarrels, leaving one or both parties sadly disillusioned.[18]

Since God made Eve, a woman, to be Adam's life partner, it is not surprising that people who go against God's plan and attempt to form permanent homosexual relationships find it almost impossible to stay together. God made Eve with a personality that complemented Adam's. The intertwining of the male and female personalities is essential to any happy and fulfilling sexual relationship.

Although some homosexuals recognize the ugliness of the homosexual subculture, most feel trapped in this degenerate life-style. Some "sympathetic" psychologists proclaim that "once a homosexual, always a homosexual." However, this viewpoint is not based on scientific evidence. Even though many psychiatrists state that a person's sexual orientation is fixed by the age of four or five, not a single study has been able to evaluate five-year-olds and predict which ones had already developed a homosexual orientation. Although a person's early experiences are very important, they do not etch his sexual preference in stone. In fact, many instances of complete reversal of sexual orientation have been published in the literature.

Harvard psychiatrist Dr. Lee Birk recently reported his results from counseling fourteen men who strongly desired to establish a proper heterosexual sex drive. He was successful in "solidly" transforming the orientation of ten of fourteen highly motivated homosexual men so that they initiated and maintained "stable and apparently happy marriages."[19]

Listen to psychiatrist Dr. Judd Marmor:

> The general view in the gay community that treatment is never successful is without foundation. The fact that most homosexual preferences are probably learned and not inborn means that, in the presence of strong motivation to change, they are open to modification, and clinical experience confirms this. . . . [However], the resistance to giving up a behavioral pattern that is a major, if not the main, source of a person's erotic satisfaction is understandably enormous; and the fact that somewhere between 25 and 50 percent of homosexuals who seek to change their main sexual orientation are able to do so is more of a tribute to the strength of their motivation than it is to the specific therapeutic approach involved.[20]

Although strong motivation is necessary, many practicing homosexuals need little therapy to become actively heterosexual. As teenagers, over half of homosexual men have experienced youthful romances with girls.[21] About one-third have had heterosexual sex dreams. An astounding 64 percent of the more overt homosexuals have experienced heterosexual intercourse; nine out of ten of these men successfully attained orgasm. Of the 20 percent of practicing homosexuals who have been married, 78 percent had sex more than once per week during their first year of marriage. About half of these men had children from their first marriage and 43 percent had been married for over five years. An astounding 57 percent rated their first marriage as moderately to very happy, and only 20 percent of their marriage breakups were due to a lack of interest in heterosexual intercourse. Only one out of three men often resorted to homosexual fantasies during marital coitus.[22]

Homosexuality, however, is not a recent phenomenon. It was practiced throughout the ancient world——by Roman emperors, mythological heroes, Greek philosophers, and the ancient Egyptians. As part of their ceremonial worship to the goddess Isis, the Egyptian "priests" (actually they were just male prostitutes) would engage in sex with the men who came to "worship." This debauched form of "worship" was found throughout the Mediterranean region where this goddess was variously known as Ishtar, Mylitta, Aphrodite, and Venus.

Among a people who "worshiped" their goddess Isis with such debauchery, Moses grew up. From the record, however, we read that Moses did not include such venereal-disease-spreading lewdity in the religious practices of the Hebrews. Rather he recorded the words of God Almighty, "Do not lie with a man as one lies with a woman; that is detestable" (Leviticus 18:22 NIV). The Law of God forbade homosexual practices. Thus, the Israelites could remain free of these wicked religious practices and free of the many diseases spread by promiscuous homosexual encounters.

Many in our society have chosen to disobey this command. They have rejected the precept of God recorded by Paul: ". . . Neither the sexually immoral . . . nor male prostitutes nor homosexual offenders . . . will inherit the kingdom of God" (1 Corinthians 6:9,10 NIV). Because of their disobedience they have brought upon themselves and upon our society a plague of old and new venereal diseases.

But men need not remain slaves to these wicked desires, for Paul continues: "And that is what some of you were [i.e., homosexuals]. But you were washed, you were sanctified, you were justified in the name of the Lord Jesus Christ and by the Spirit of our God" (1 Corinthians 6:11 NIV). God does not desert men to futile human attempts at obeying His commandments; for He gives His Holy Spirit, who vitalizes and empowers the believer in Christ Jesus to overcome the vice of homosexuality. Jesus Christ is the alternative for those who engage in the venereal-disease-spreading lewdities of the "alternative life-styles."

Thus, God frees believers from the vices of Satan and allows them to partake in His promise: "None of these diseases," which He had brought upon the [practicing homosexual] Egyptians and which He has brought upon the practicing homosexuals of our modern age.

Chapter Eight

Circumventing Cancer With Circumspect Circumcision

 Forty-two-year-old Jack Schmidt shifted his weight nervously on the examining room table as I washed my hands. "Well, what brings you here," I asked. I had noticed that he had not come to see me in over five years.

"Doc, I've got this lump that I guess you should take a look at. It's probably nothing, but I've been getting kinda worried about it." Jack proceeded to show me a golf-ball-sized tumor that looked something like a small head of cauliflower with a large cratered ulcer in the middle.

"How long have you had this?" I asked.

"Oh, several weeks—at least."

"How about six months?"

Jack looked startled, "Yeh, I guess. How did you know, Doc."

The next day, we admitted Jack to the hospital; and as I had guessed, the pathologist diagnosed the surgical sample of his tumor to be squamus-cell carcinoma of the penis with metastases to the lymph nodes of the groin. When I broke the news to Jack, he covered his face with his hands and sobbed, "Why me?"

Why Jack? He had waited too long to get help. If he had seen me six months earlier while the cancer was still localized, his treatment would have resulted almost certainly in a cure. But at this late stage, we could offer him little hope. Studies have shown that over one-third of the victims of this cancer put off seeking treatment until their cancer has reached an incurable state.[1]

Despite radical surgery—removal of the penis and the lymph nodes of the groin—Jack died about two years later, leaving behind two boys and their mother.

What makes his death even more tragic is the fact that medical science has now proved that cancer of the penis is almost entirely preventable by following an instruction that God gave to Abraham over four thousand years ago.

The history of this recognition is intriguing. In 1932, Dr. A. L. Wolbarst of New York reviewed the records of 1,103 cases of cancer of the penis. Among all these cases there was not even one Jew.[2] Indeed, cancer of the penis is so astoundingly rare among Jews that its very occurrence warrants publication in a medical journal. Since Dr. Wolbarst's study, only six cases of such cancers in Jews have been reported.[3]

Why are Jewish men almost entirely free of this lethal cancer? Medical researchers have found that this spectacular freedom results from the practice of circumcision, instituted by God over four thousand years ago.

Jewish men are not the only men "immune" to this disease. Researchers have found that any man circumcised in infancy will also enjoy this "immunity." In three large studies covering 521 cases of cancer of the penis, not a single circumcised man was found.[4] What makes this statistic even more startling is the finding that in the age group at risk for this cancer about one-half of men were circumcised. Thus, one would have expected about 260 cases (half of 521) to occur in men who were circumcised—instead, they found none.

From India comes another convincing study.[5] In India there are four major religious groups: Hindus, Christians, Parsees, and Moslems. Moslems circumcise their sons between the ages of three and twelve, but none of the other groups practice circumcision. Among the Hindu, Christian, and Parsee men—cancers of the penis make up 330 of every 10,000 cancers; but among circumcised Moslems—only 15 out of 10,000 cancers are diagnosed as cancer of the penis. The cause for most of these 15 cancers is probably the Moslem practice of delaying circumcision until a boy is several years old.

Although cancer of the penis is fairly rare in the United States, the actual rate of this cancer in uncircumcised men is about 1 in 600.[6] Thus, if none of the 1.8 million American boys born each year were circumcised, one would expect about 3,000 of these boys to have penile cancer during their lifetimes and about 1,000 to die from this disease.

How does circumcision protect men from penile cancer? Most experts feel that these cancers are caused by smegma, a filthy and foul-smelling paste of bacteria and dead cells trapped under the foreskin. By circumcision (*circum*, "around"; *cision*, "cutting"), the foreskin is removed, eliminating the small pouch on the end of the penis where smegma accumulates.

The American Academy of Pediatrics states, "Circumcision, properly performed, eliminates much of the need for careful penile hygiene. If circumcision is not elected, [however], the necessity for lifelong penile hygiene should be discussed with the parents."[7] Routine retraction of the foreskin and careful cleansing of the penile head would cleanse the penis of smegma and, theoretically, eliminate the risk of penile cancer. Thus, the American Academy of Pediatrics holds "that there are no valid medical indications for circumcision in the neonatal period."[8]

This recommendation, however, is based on the erroneous assumption that if you tell a boy to wash something, he will do it. Most mothers have had the exasperating experience of repeatedly sending a son to the bathroom to wash behind his ears. In fact, one study found that only one out of four uncircumcised teenage boys who had a retractable foreskin actually practiced personal penile hygiene.

In recent years a tremendous amount of debate about the pros and cons of circumcision has appeared in medical journals. Articles entitled "Penile Plunder"[9] and "The Rape of the Phallus"[10] underscore the emotional opposition of some physicians. Others have pointed to the origins of the anticircumcision movement as growing out of "guilt-induced anxiety leading to a fear of genital injury," and they further state that "the catalytic element for the anticircumcision swell lies in the current aura of protest. . . . Movements abound to save wild horses, polar bears, islands, and lakes. The establishment is seen as a universally bad guy. In this atmosphere the male infant is easily and emotionally envisaged as helpless and unmarred——as indeed he is."[11]

The literature of the anticircumcision crusade has recently received the addition of a book by Edward Wallerstein. Although Mr. Wallerstein refers to over 450 different authors, he fails to quote any of the statistics that I have just mentioned regarding penile carcinoma. Instead, he reasons: "The argument that carcinoma of the penis will be prevented by circumcision is hardly valid, for there are cases of this disease in circumcised males."[12] However, it is his reasoning that is invalid. Medical literature finds penile carcinoma to be extremely rare, but not nonexistent, in circumcised males. His statement is analogous to saying, "Since men may die (however rarely) from breast cancer, men are not protected from this disease," or,

"Since nonsmokers may die (however rarely) from lung cancer, they are not protected from this cancer." The fact is that, even in the United States, uncircumcised men have well over a hundredfold greater risk of penile carcinoma.

Some doctors who recognize that circumcision prevents penile cancer point out that circumcision is surgery, so it involves a certain amount of risk. The largest study to date of the risk of circumcision found, in 500,000 newborn circumcisions, only one death—which occurred after a ritual circumcision in a home and was complicated by a delay in obtaining a transfusion.[13] If these 500,000 newborns had not been circumcised, about 830 would have come down with penile carcinoma and about 275 would have died from this disease.[14] The statistics speak for themselves.

If we have these statistics in the United States where most people practice daily bathing of their bodies, imagine the problem in more primitive cultures where washing the body, let alone the head of the penis, is an extremely rare event and where penile cancer is invariably fatal. While I worked in Africa, I was appalled at the high prevalence of lethal penile cancer among the uncircumcised nationals. In fact, penile cancer makes up 18 percent of the male cancers in China—a land of poor hygiene and uncircumcised males.[15] To such a people, the nomadic household of Abraham, God gave the command to circumcise every male.

Even the most adamant opponents of circumcision recognize that this procedure is necessary for many boys who cannot retract their foreskin. Circumcision facilitates cleanliness by eliminating the need for scrupulous penile hygiene. In Canada where only 50 percent of newborns are circumcised, over 10,000 therapeutic circumcisions are performed on boys who have passed infancy. For these surgeries, the boys are "put to sleep" under general anesthesia, which carries with it a risk of death of about one in 10,000. Thus, one would expect about one Canadian boy per year to die from therapeutic circumcision. However, if all of the 90,000 uncircumcised boys had been circumcised as infants, an average of over five years would have passed between deaths from these circumcisions.[16]

Serious risk remains even if the doctor performs the surgery by numbing the area with a local anesthetic. Recently, two doctors reported two young men who became permanently impotent following circumcision with a local anesthetic.[17]

Also, these circumcisions done on older boys and men are much more expensive than infant circumcisions—due to additional hospital stays, doctor's costs, and work loss. One author has estimated that if all Canadian boys were circumcised as infants, it would result in a saving of over $18 million per year.[18]

Thus, we see that routine infant circumcision is cost effective and prevents deaths from penile cancer and delayed surgery.

After many laborious years of study, medical science has demonstrated the most effective way for preventing the deadly squamus-cell carcinoma of the penis. Science did not arrive at this conclusion because of any laboratory steam it had generated; rather, it was carried forward by a long train of statistics—statistics that existed only because many generations of Jews and Moslems had faithfully followed the command that God gave to their father Abraham.[19]

In the first edition of this book, I cited the evidence that cancer of the uterine cervix (the tip of the uterus that caps off the vagina) was primarily a disease of sexual partners of uncircumcised males. In the intervening years, however, cervical cancer has been more firmly related to multiple sexual partners. One study of the death certificates of 13,000 celibate nuns did not turn up even a single cancer of the cervix.[20] A recent study found evidence of venereal-wart viruses in 73 of 80 women who had cervical cancer.[21] Thus, it seems that cervical cancer is, for the most part, a result of venereal disease; and therefore following biblical moral principles would probably wipe out this common cancer.

One night while I was in Africa, the chief of a local tribe awakened me and asked me to perform a circumcision on his twelve-year-old son. I did the procedure in the operating room. The chief requested that I tell no one about the clandestine surgery; and for my payment, he invited me to attend the ritual circumcision for the rest of the twelve-year-old boys in the tribe. Two weeks later, I arrived at the site for the ritual. For several hours the twelve-year-olds threw eerie shadows as they danced around a large bonfire. Then they lined up against a fence. With a large butcher knife in hand, the witch doctor, his body painted in oranges and reds and his face covered with a grotesque wooden mask, approached the trembling boys. Suddenly, he grasped the foreskin of the first boy in line, leaped three feet into the air, shrieked a cry of terrifying vengeance, and severed the foreskin from the unsuspecting boy. He repeated this procedure on the rest of the boys. With the chief's son he then entered a small hut where he repeated the sound effects, but not the procedure. While all of the other boys were moaning in excruciating pain, the chief's son exited the hut defiantly. He jumped on a donkey and rode into the village. Whereupon, all of the members of the tribe recognized the superior character of the heir to the chiefdom.

What about pain? No one would deny that circumcision is a painful experience, but the amount of pain suffered is related to the age of the male being circumcised. The most careful study of this matter was conducted by Dr. Joseph Katz. In infants up to three weeks old, he observed pain and irritability only at the immediate time of surgery. However, infants from four weeks to three months old were still irritable during the night following surgery; children between three months to one year were irritable for three to four days; and adults suffered pain and discomfort for at least a week.[22]

Moreover, circumcisions done on older boys or adults also carry the psychological trauma of removing a private part of their bodies. For example, one study found that boys circumcised beween the ages of four and seven viewed the operation as an attack on their bodies, and this procedure resulted in an increase in their aggressive emotions even several days after surgery.[23] Even thinking about the procedure produces discomfort in most men.

Thus, the least physically and psychologically traumatic time to circumcise a male child is sometime during the first few days of life.

Does it make any difference what day is chosen within these first few days? In a pediatric journal we read, "The greatest risk of hemorrhage occurs between two and seven days of life."[24] A pediatric textbook elaborates, "Hemorrhages at this time, though often inconsequential, are sometimes extensive; they may produce serious damage to internal organs, especially to the brain, and cause death from shock and exsanguination."[25]

At birth the baby's intestines contain no bacteria. Between the fifth to seventh day of life, these bacteria begin to proliferate and produce the important vitamin K. This vitamin goes to the liver where it plays an important part in forming four different clotting proteins. If any one of these proteins is missing, serious bleeding may result. In most normal babies blood levels of all four proteins decrease quickly after birth because infants are vitamin K deficient. Today, however, doctors boost the infant's clotting system by giving newborn babies shots of vitamin K; thus, medical science has eliminated this potentially serious bleeding disorder.

One of the proteins dependent on vitamin K is called prothrombin. The following graph, based on data collected before the era of routine vitamin K shots, shows that by the third day of a baby's life the available prothrombin is only 30 percent of normal. By the eighth day, however, we see that the available prothrombin skyrockets to 110 percent of the adult level. It soon levels off to normal (100 percent). An average eight-day-old baby has more available prothrombin than on any other day of his life. Thus, the safest day in a male's entire life to perform a circumcision is the eighth day.

We should commend the many hundreds of workers who labored at great expense over a number of years and found that the safest day to perform circumcision is the eighth. Yet, as we congratulate medical science, we almost hear the pages of the Bible rustling. When we turn to Genesis 17:12, we read God's words to Abraham,

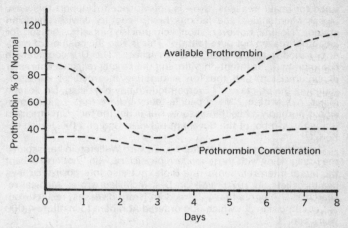

FIGURE 12: Average concentration of available prothrombin in normal infants during the first week of life. From data of Owen, Hoffman, Ziffren and Smith.[26]

". . . every male among you who is eight days old must be circumcised . . ." (NIV).

Abraham did not pick the eighth day after many centuries of trial-and-error experiments, although many modern physicians think otherwise. For example, we read in a 1982 edition of the Cecil *Textbook of Medicine*, "The vitamin K-deficient state lasts for three to five days and may be the reason why the Israelites did not circumcise their babies until the eighth day."[27] However, in babies who are not given vitamin K shots, only one in 200 to 400 babies suffers a bleeding disorder.[28] Thus, in order to determine that the eighth day was the safest day to circumcise, the Hebrews—a primitive, nomadic desert-dwelling people—would have had to conduct immense carefully designed experiments, including thousands of circumcisions performed on each day of the newborns' lives. Why not accept the Bible's statement that God spoke to Abraham?

Neither Abraham nor any of his company from the ancient city of Ur in the Chaldees had ever been circumcised; and although some of the Middle Eastern peoples did practice circumcision, historians feel that infant circumcision was unique to the Israelites. Thus, the eighth day was not picked by some genius in statistical analysis but by the Creator of vitamin K.

Although it is often thought that Jewish circumcision was instituted for health reasons, there is no evidence to support this view. Moses Maimonides, the famous twelfth-century Jewish physician stated, "No one, however, should circumcise himself or his son for any other reason but pure faith."[29] This is also the position of modern Orthodox rabbis such as Erich Isaac: "The Orthodox Jewish community . . . is intent on affirming the strictly religious character of circumcision, and thus on eliminating the medical aura surrounding the practice."[30] Even a modern-day physician, Dr. Joseph Miller, has written: "Many people today believe that . . . circumcision is primarily a health measure. This is not the fact. Circumcision . . . is the symbol of the Covenant between God and the Jewish nation."[31]

Using these and other quotes Mr. Edward Wallerstein has scolded me for agreeing with those modern physicians who "not only accept the literal interpretation of the Bible, but also interpose their own health beliefs. In 1970 [sic], Dr. S. I. McMillen wrote: 'Medical researchers . . . agree that . . . freedom [from diseases] results from . . . circumcision . . . which God ordered Abraham to institute 4,000 years ago.' "[32]

I grant him that God may have had other reasons than the health of his people in mind when He instituted circumcision; but the fact remains that the ancient Hebrews, whether they knew it or not, gained health benefits from following God's command. Just as washing and separation after touching the dead were practiced solely because this was a command of God, so the Hebrews followed God's command of circumcision. This is true of all of God's commandments; if we obey them, even if we do not know the specific reason for the command, we will reap temporal and eternal benefits.

The inspiration of the biblical account becomes even more obvious when we take a look at the changes that the Jews made in the circumcision ritual over the years. During the few centuries preceding Christ, the Greeks attempted to convert Jews to paganism. These "converts" blistered the remainder of their foreskins. The resulting scar tissue formed an artificial foreskin, thus obliterating the appearance of circumcision. In order to prevent this practice, the ritual-circumcision surgeon ripped away all of the remaining foreskin with his sharpened fingernails.[33] The resulting ragged, filthy wound ensured a high rate of infection. By the seventh century A.D., many Jews added a second change to the ritual. In addition to scraping with his fingernails, the ritual surgeon moistened his lips with wine, placed the infant's penis in his mouth, and sucked the blood from the ragged wound. Even the great Jewish physician Maimonides "staunchly supported this procedure as a prophylactic measure against inflammation."[34] The mouth is a perfect medium for growing bacteria, however, so this procedure increased the frequency and severity of inflammation from infections. Today, in backward Israeli villages, fatal cases of gangrene, tuberculosis, and tetanus still result from this filthy ritual. In order to save one boy, doctors had to amputate the infant's penis.[35] Why don't modern scientists give us some explanation for the empirical origins of these disease-producing rituals? Why don't they note the "careful observations" that the Jews must have made in order to come up with these deadly practices? The answer is simple: like almost all health rituals of primitive peoples, these rituals are based on whimsical superstition not on scientific observation or on the commands of God—so they inevitably have serious and deleterious effects.

God stated that circumcision was to be done with "flint knives" (Joshua 5:2). God simply commanded that the foreskins be cut off with these knives. Scraping with sharpened fingernails or sucking with a filthy mouth were man's additions. The use of this particular knife is also interesting, for in sharpening a flint knife one chips away at the stone until one has a sharp edge—exposing new uncontaminated stone. Thus, a newly sharpened flint knife is practically sterile. Isn't it interesting that Moses did not specify one of the common Egyptian ointments, containing animal dung, in order to "speed up the healing"?

As circumcision symbolized God's old Covenant with the Children of Abraham, so circumcision symbolizes God's New Covenant with the Believers in Jesus. This circumcision of the New Covenant, however, cannot be performed with a flint knife. As Paul said:

> In him [Christ] you were also circumcised, in the putting off of the sinful nature, not with a circumcision done by the hands of men but with the circumcision done by Christ. . . . Put to death, therefore, whatever belongs to your earthly nature: sexual immorality, impurity, lust, evil desires and greed, which is idolatry. . . . now you must rid yourselves of all such things as these: anger, rage, malice, slander, and filthy language from your lips. Do not lie to each other, since you have taken off your old self with its practices.
>
> Colossians 2:11; 3:5,8,9 NIV

As God required circumcision of the Jew, so today He requires circumcision of His people. The circumcision of the Old Covenant removed the foreskin that provided a medium for cancer-causing smegma; the circumcision of the New Covenant removes the emotions (anger, malice, greed, and so forth) that provide a medium for disease-causing stress. Such circumcision frees man from these unlovely emotions—emotions that produce undue stress, a cause of many, and an aggravation of almost all, diseases.

While physical circumcision of men's filthy foreskins prevents cancer, spiritual circumcision of our evil natures prevents a far greater number of important diseases.

Bodily circumcision is not required today, because it was instituted by God as a sign of a much greater circumcision—a circumcision that Christ now performs on the minds and hearts of His followers.[36] Circumcision of the body looked forward to circumcision of the spirit.[37] Is it not exciting and appropriate that both the type and the fulfillment of God's Covenant with man prevent deadly disease?

As God required bodily circumcision for membership in the Children of Israel, so God requires Christ's circumcision for membership in the Body of Christ: "Those who belong to Christ Jesus have crucified the sinful nature with its passions and desires" (Galatians 5:24 NIV). Only after Jesus has performed this divine surgery can a person enjoy fellowship with God and the promise of God—"none of these diseases."

Chapter Nine

Upset Mind—
Sick Body

As I walked into the examining room, five-year-old Helen Seibert cowered on her mother's lap and hid her face in her mother's blouse. Her mother answered my inquiring look: "Doctor, Helen's been vomiting every day for the past six weeks. Everything I give her comes back up. She began to vomit the day after Labor Day."

Helen had entered kindergarten on the day after Labor Day. The area elementary school with its hundreds of new faces had overwhelmed Helen, for she lived far up in the mountains where there were few children to play with.

Why was she vomiting? Her anxiety on separating from her mother and being thrown in among so many strangers had sent hurried impulses along nerves from emotional centers in her brain to tighten the muscular outlet of her stomach. As a result much of her food could not pass into the intestines, and it had no place to go but up where it came from. Little Helen had already missed four weeks of school.

After examining Helen, I explained the problem to Mrs. Seibert and emphasized that Helen must go to school no matter how much she protested about nausea, vomiting, or bellyaches. This treatment may seem harsh and extreme, but doctors now agree that this is the only way to handle the distressing and common problem of separation anxiety. Allowing children to stay home can so reenforce this behavior that some children are never able to attend school and never receive an education.

When Helen realized that she had no choice—despite her symptoms, she had to go to school—she learned to cope with the many children at school. Because she soon formed friendships with schoolmates, she no longer suffered such extreme anxiety upon the daily separation from her mother. By first grade, Helen even began to look forward to going to school.

Such trouble is not confined to children. On a Saturday night, eighteen-year-old Donna Cole told me she had been vomiting and suffering from severe abdominal cramps and diarrhea for five days. Her trouble had begun about an hour after she had left the dentist's office.

The dentist had told this attractive girl that she must have all of her teeth pulled and be fitted with false ones. Result: a tempest in her emotional centers. Nerve impulses from her brain quickly initiated and perpetuated severe vomiting, cramps, and diarrhea.

Although she insisted on a series of very expensive and uncomfortable tests, I assured her that her problem was probably quite temporary and that further tests were not yet warranted. I then reviewed her "separate" problem of losing all of her teeth. I arranged for her to meet with a cheerleader who had lost her front teeth in an automobile accident, to discuss the adjustment to denture wearing. Her talk with this popular cheerleader allayed her fears, and she recovered, "almost miraculously." When I later told her of the true nature of her problem, she wouldn't believe me.

Equally surprised was Elaine Johnson when she discovered that her headaches came from anxiety about losing her boyfriend, Bill Landry; Bill found out that it was not the professor's assignment that aggravated his asthma, but his griping about it; and the professor who gave the assignment could not figure out why his arthritis became so much worse when he corrected his students' antagonistic papers.

These cases illustrate a most intriguing subject in modern medicine. With every passing year, we obtain a wider comprehension of the ability of the mind (*psyche*) to produce varied disturbances of the body (*soma*); hence the term *psychosomatic*. Invisible emotional tension in the mind can produce striking visible changes in the body, changes that can become serious and fatal.

This concept should give us a new perspective on conditions that are often contemptuously referred to as "being in the head." Obviously such conditions as vomiting, diarrhea, asthma, and arthritis are not "in the head"; yet these and scores of other serious diseases are triggered or aggravated by tension in the mind.

A large percentage of most physicians' practices are made up of patients whose illnesses are directly or indirectly the result of emotional stress.

At the beginning of this century, infection was the most important cause of serious, debilitating, and chronic disease. Now eighty years later, mental stress has taken its place. In fact, stress often reduces a person's ability to fight off infections. One study done at West Point showed that cadets who were under greater academic stress, as measured by low grades or parental pressure, were much more likely to suffer from infectious mononucleosis—more commonly known as "mono."[1]

You have probably noticed that you often come down with a cold or sore throat after several nights of reduced sleep or several days of increased work.

How can certain emotions cause bodily diseases such as strokes to the brain, fatal clots in the heart, bleeding ulcers of the intestinal tract, spasms of the back muscles and gangrene of leg tissue—to mention only a few of the conditions? The brain, where all emotional stress is processed, is the control center of the entire body. From the brain millions of nerve fibers course out to every organ in the body. Chemicals released from these nerve fibers control or influence every chemical reaction in every organ of the body. Because our health is dependent on the proper balance of all of these chemical reactions, it is no wonder that emotional upset in our brains can disrupt chemical reactions in a far-removed organ and cause disease.

The brain produces these widespread changes by means of three principal mechanisms: by changing the amount of blood flowing to an organ; by affecting the secretions of certain glands; and by changing the tension of muscles.

Remember the last time that you saw a person blush. That was an example of an emotion—embarrassment—increasing the blood-flow to an organ—the skin. The emotions of anxiety or hate can so increase the amount of blood within a rigid skull that migraine headache and vomiting result from the irritation of the brain.

Irritation in the emotional centers is also directed toward the glands of the body. Remember the first time you had to speak before an audience and recall how parched your mouth became. Alarm messages had gone from your emotional centers, which dried up the salivary-gland secretions. It is indeed hard to speak when the mouth is dry. Even experienced speakers may experience emotional strain and consequent drying of the saliva. That is why a glass of water is often placed on the speaker's rostrum.

Emotional tension affects the secretion of the ovaries in a variety of ways. Disturbances in the centers of the brain responsible for producing chemicals that stimulate the ovaries can cause a cessation of the menses, bleeding of the uterus, loss of fertility, bloating during menstruation, and even imitation of pregnancy—where a woman gets all the symptoms of early pregnancy, including morning nausea, ankle swelling, and increased breast size. These women put on a tremendous amount of weight; and by thrusting out their bellies, they can even look pregnant. Several years ago one of these women actually went into "labor" in a Philadelphia hospital, and because the doctors could not hear the baby's heartbeat they decided to deliver the baby by an emergency Cesarean section. Fortunately, an alert physician thought of the true diagnosis just in time to avert the surgical opening of her nonpregnant abdomen.

Emotional stress can affect muscle tone. All of us have felt our muscles tightening up when we become frightened, frustrated, or furious. Tightened muscles can produce pain, as you can demonstrate by clenching your fist tightly for a few minutes. Thus, you can see why people with chronic anxieties suffer a great deal with severe tension headaches, stemming from neck and head muscles in spasm.

One afternoon my secretary told me that a distraught young couple were waiting for me in my office. I recognized them immediately as the young couple who had seen me for a premarital exam several months earlier. I greeted them and asked them what they wished to discuss. There was a long pause, but then Jim blurted out, "It's Mary. Uhh—she's—uhh, well, you know—she's frigid. . . ."

Mary cut in, "Doctor—please—you've got to help us. Jim says he's going to get a divorce."

I asked Jim to leave the room and then discussed the problem with Mary. She told me that whenever they had tried to have sexual intercourse she had experienced severe cutting pain. She told me that she would never have sex again, but she wondered if there was some drug that I could give Jim that would satisfy his "animal desires." Although they had previously turned down my offer for premarital counseling, I quickly realized that Mary suffered from a lack of information about the proper role of sex in marriage and a host of misinformation about her body and about sexual technique. All of this misinformation had caused a tremendous amount of anxiety for Mary. Upon the act of sex, this anxiety was converted into an intense spasm of the muscles around her vagina (vaginismus), and this spasm had resulted in terrible pain.

After several weeks of counseling about the proper role of sex in marriage with concurrent practicing of prescribed intimate exercises in their own home, they returned to my office. Their grateful smiles assured me that there would be no divorce.

Emotional turmoil can also manifest itself through pain over the heart. One day I received an urgent call from a woman. "Hurry up, Doc," she gasped. "Jerry's had another heart attack. I think he's going to die this time." I rushed over to her house and found Jerry lying on the floor, gasping for breath and suffering real pain over his heart. He looked like a person dying from heart trouble, but he was in no danger.

Every three or four months Jerry's wife called me with the same urgent message, and Jerry was admitted to the hospital to rule out serious heart disease. When Jerry returned home, his wife would dote on her "invalid" husband for several months; but when he began to "recover," they would begin to fight. The arguments would get longer and more acrimonious until Jerry's subconscious allowed him to escape from the fracas; and he would fall to the floor, stricken with a "heart attack."

During World War I men with such a condition were great liabilities in the army, and the condition was named "soldier's heart." When World War II came along, special efforts were made to weed out such men. In fact, ten times as many men were rejected for this emotional type of heart pain as for all other heart diseases. Physicians also saw many civilians suffering from "soldier's heart" during the war. After every bombing of English cities, tens of thousands were unable to go to work because of chest pains.

Fatal heart attacks can also be triggered by anger, depression, and anxiety. In fact, anxiety probably places more stress on the heart than any other stimulus, including physical exercise and fatigue.

The effect of psychological stress on the heart was observed in Athens, Greece, after the 1981 earthquake. During the three days after this quake twenty Athenians died from "atherosclerotic heart disease." Contrast this number with the average death rate from this disease in Athens—only 2.6 deaths per day.[2] This study demonstrates the striking effect of anxiety on deaths from coronary artery disease.

The magnitude of influence of stress on the human body can be demonstrated by a partial listing of diseases that medical scientists have observed to be associated with emotional stress. Since much of this research has not been widely disseminated, even within the medical profession, I have included selected references for those who wish to look into the way stress relates to a specific disease. Of course it should not be assumed that the emotional factor is the sole cause or irritant in any of these cases:

Disorders of the Digestive System
    Ulcers of the stomach and intestines
    Ulcerative colitis[3]

Loss of appetite
Hiccups
Irritable bowel syndrome
Achalasia (a type of swallowing difficulty)[4]

Disorders of the Circulatory System
High blood pressure[5]
Paroxysmal tachycardia
Atherosclerosis
Coronary thrombosis or spasm
Strokes[6]
Abnormal heart rhythms[7]
Migraine headaches[8]
Angina pectoris[9]

Disorders of the Genito-Urinary System
Lack of menstruation
Vaginismus
Frequent and painful urination
Impotence
Dysfunctional uterine bleeding[10]
False pregnancy[11]
Infertility[12]

Disorders of the Nervous System
Headaches of several types
Epileptic attacks
Psychoneuroses
Hyperventilation syndrome

Disorders of Glands
Hyperthyroidism[13]
Diabetes (insulin dependent diabetes of juvenile onset)[14]
Chronic pancreatitis[15]

Allergic Disorders
Hives
Hay fever
Asthmatic attacks[16]

Muscle-Joint Disorders
Backache
Tension headache
Rheumatoid arthritis[17]
Myasthenia gravis[18]

Infections
Infectious mononucleosis[19]
Chronic tuberculosis[20]
"Strep" throat[21]

Inflammatory and Skin Diseases
Neurodermatitis
Raynaud's disease[22]
Systemic lupus erythematosus (SLE)[23]

Nutritional and Drug Disorders
Anorexia nervosa
Obesity
Drug addictions (including alcohol, cigarettes, marijuana, and caffeine)
Vitamin abuse

Cancers
Lung cancer[24]
Gastric cancer[25]
Childhood cancers[26]
Cancers of many types[27]

Again, I must emphasize that few of these diseases are caused or triggered solely by psychological stress. Other factors such as genetic composition, chronological age, previous immunizations, and nutritional state are involved not only in determining the type of disease but also the severity of the disease in any one person.

A list of such length in no way supports the tenets of "Christian Science," which holds that all diseases are "just in your head." This view is neither Christian nor scientific, for it is refuted by both Scripture and modern science. However, we must also realize that emotional factors are involved in our adaptation to or recovery from any disease.

A proper view of the influence of stress on disease takes into consideration both modern scientific evidence and the promise of Scripture:

> A righteous man may have many troubles,
> but the Lord delivers him from them all.
> Psalms 34:19 NIV

In the following chapters we will examine the meaning of this promise: how we can become more righteous and, as we do so, how the Lord will deliver us from our troubles.

Chapter Ten

It's Not What You Eat— It's What Eats You

 Big Bill Brandon was a very likable fellow——when he didn't "fly off the handle." When one of his men at the plant messed up an assignment, Bill would get furious and castigate the bungler with the sharpest expletives in his voluminous foul vocabulary. But the abuse he hurled at the other fellow always seemed to boomerang on poor Bill and eventually put him in bed. Then his wife would call me to the house. It was such an oft-repeated story that she would merely open the door of the house, broadly sweep her arm toward Bill's bedroom, laconically shrug her shoulders in apology, and belatedly force a smile of welcome. "Doc, he has been vomiting for two weeks straight, but he wouldn't let me call you until this morning."

I couldn't help feeling sorry for big Bill as he lay on his belly across his bed. His eyes were big, red, and desperate. Every few seconds he pleadingly moaned. Of course, he had been studied and x-rayed in several hospitals where he had spent a small fortune. His trouble was always brought on by anger, which tightened the outlet of his stomach and caused the intractable vomiting. These episodes had become so frequent and so severe that Bill had been missing work two or three days a week. He was now barely earning enough to support his wife and eight children.

Bill's duodenum (the first part of the small intestine) must have

105

had a stainless-steel lining, because after such a buildup of acid in the stomach, many people develop ulcers. In fact, it is generally agreed in medical circles that duodenal ulcers, often mistakenly called stomach ulcers, are caused not so much by what the person eats as by what "eats the person." Of course, after ulcers develop they are aggravated by certain foods and emotional upsets.

The attitudes that can cause disease include fear, jealousy, envy, rage, resentment, and hatred. Also included are other emotions when in excess: sorrow, ambition, frustration, and need for love or security. Observe that these disease-producing emotions are concerned with protecting and coddling the self, and they could be summarized under one title—self-centeredness.

Centuries before modern psychiatry discovered that certain emotions were important factors in the development of many diseases, the Apostle Paul condemned these emotions: "The activities of the lower nature are obvious. Here is a list: sexual immorality . . . hatred, quarrelling, jealousy, bad temper, rivalry, factions, party-spirit, envy, drunkenness, orgies and things like that . . ." (Galatians 5:19–21 YOUNG CHURCHES). But God did not intend for man to be controlled by these emotions so Paul added: "Those who belong to Christ Jesus have crucified the sinful nature with its passions and desires" (Galatians 5:24 NIV).

Dr. William Sadler was also impressed by the close connection between the sinful "activities of the lower nature" and many diseases of the physical body. We read:

> No one can appreciate so fully as a doctor the amazingly large percentage of human disease and suffering which is directly traceable to worry, fear, conflict, immorality, dissipation, and ignorance—to unwholesome thinking and unclean living. The sincere acceptance of the principles and teachings of Christ with respect to the life of mental peace and joy, the life of unselfish thought and clean living, would . . . wipe out more than half the difficulties, diseases, and sorrows of the human race. In other words, more than one half of the present affliction of mankind could be prevented by the tremendous prophylactic power of actually living up to the personal and practical spirit of the real teachings of Christ.
>
> The teachings of Jesus applied to our modern civilization—understandingly applied, not merely nominally accepted—would so purify, uplift, and vitalize us that the race would immediately stand out as a new order of beings, possessing superior mental power and increased moral force. Irrespective of the future rewards of living,

laying aside all discussion of future life, it would pay any man or woman to live the Christian life just for the mental and moral rewards it affords here in this present world. Some day man may awake to the fact that the teachings of Christ are potent and powerful in preventing and curing disease.[1]

Shakespeare knew enough about human nature to recognize that people can become sick from unconfessed sin. It was the memory of the murder of Duncan that produced psychosomatic overtones in Lady Macbeth; for when Macbeth asked the physician about her illness, he replied:

> Not so sick, my lord,
> As she is troubled with thick-coming fancies,
> That keep her from her rest.[2]

The doctor was then asked the same question put to many a physician today:

> Canst thou not minister to a mind diseased,
> Pluck from the memory of a rooted sorrow,
> Raze out the written troubles of the brain
> And with some sweet oblivious antidote
> Cleanse the stuff'd bosom of that perilous stuff
> Which weighs upon the heart?[3]

A man about forty years of age came into my office one evening. His stomach was bothering him and he could not sleep. His ailment had disturbed his life so much that he thought that he might have to give up his job and become unable to support his family of three. When he came into my office, I did not detect any bodily ailment, but I did recognize that he was on the verge of serious nervous breakdown. After telling me about some of the physical factors that he believed to be at the root of his trouble, he said, "Doctor Mac, I have done some bad things. Things that would put me behind bars."

I recognized that we were dealing with something far beyond the reach of a tranquilizer. I told him so and advised him to bow his head on my desk, confess, and ask his heavenly Father for forgiveness.

He did just that, simply and earnestly. Immediately and miraculously God removed "that perilous stuff, which weighs upon the heart." The next time I saw him, several years had passed, and the man had not missed a day of work. He was happy and buoyant. His trouble had not been caused by anything he was eating; it had stemmed from guilt gnawing at his conscience.

Psychiatrist William Sadler writes, "A clear conscience is a great step toward barricading the mind against neuroticism."

Psychologist Henry C. Link also sees the connection between sin and disease: "The emphasis on sin has largely disappeared from the teachings of religion . . . at the very time when psychology has discovered its importance and extended its meaning."[4]

You may ask: "If an individual is converted and crucifies his sinful nature, will that individual then be virtually 'immune' to diseases caused by jealousy, envy, resentment, hatred, and self-centeredness?"

An episode about a person I know might answer this question. The woman was a missionary in India and had become very bitter toward the leaders who had imposed unjust and immoral conditions on the poverty-stricken people. She prayed for the people, but spent many an hour castigating the latest malevolent move of the political leaders. Let us assume she was justified in resenting the people responsible for the state of affairs; but the point is, she did resent them.

Her relentless resentment caused the glands in her stomach to secrete acid and enzymes even when they were not needed for digestion, and she developed an ulcer. One day that ulcer eroded into a large artery. She began to vomit tankards of blood. In six days she was nearly exsanguinated. Here was a Christian woman who loved the Lord and who worked full-time for the Lord. Yet she developed an ulcer and nearly died from hemorrhage—because she had forgotten that God was in control of the situation. Overvaluing her own point of view, she nourished her indignation rather than crucify her self.

By changing a few details, the same story could be told of tens of thousands of professed Christians whose improper attitudes lead to one of the diseases already listed. Consecrations made at an altar are not sufficient. We must daily crucify our selfish desires and obey all of Christ's teachings. Only then will we be free from psychosomatic diseases. As John wrote, "If anyone obeys his word, God's love is truly made complete in him. This is how we know we are in him" (1 John 2:5 NIV).

We remain human beings; and as such, we will constantly battle with our evil natures. We will still make errors in judgment and in attitudes toward others. One thing is true, however, in proportion as we understand and obey the directions in the Bible, we shall be blessed in mind and body.

Applicable here is an admonition from the Letter to the Hebrews: "Let it be your ambition to live at peace with all men and to achieve holiness 'without which no man shall see the Lord.' Be careful that none of you fails to respond to the grace which God gives, for if he does there can very easily spring up in him a bitter spirit which is not only bad in itself but can also poison the lives of many others'' (Hebrews 12:14,15 YOUNG CHURCHES).

What a person eats is not as important as the resentment, the hate, and the guilt that eat at his very being. An antacid tablet in the stomach will never reach these acids that destroy body, mind, and soul.

The Bible doesn't merely treat the disease-producing attitudes of envy, resentment, hatred, immorality, and self-centeredness. The Bible strikes at the cause: ''Those who belong to Christ have crucified their old nature with all that it loved and lusted for'' (Galatians 5:24 YOUNG CHURCHES).

Chapter Eleven

The High Cost of Getting Even

Dale Carnegie once told the story of a trip to Yellowstone Park and a visit to the place where the grizzly bears are fed.[1] He did not have to wait long before a grizzly bear came into a clearing where garbage had been dumped to entice him. The guide told the group that the grizzly bear can whip any animal in the West with the possible exceptions of the buffalo and Kodiak bear. That night, as Dale Carnegie sat with the other tourists in the bleachers, he noticed that the grizzly would only allow one animal to eat with him—the skunk. Of course, in a fight the grizzly could have thrashed any skunk. He probably resented the skunk and yearned to get even with him for his brazen impudence. But he didn't. Why? Because he knew the high cost of getting even.

Smart grizzly? Certainly much smarter than many human beings who spend weary days and sleepless nights rummaging through their polluted memories, brooding over worm-eaten resentments and scheming venomous revenge. Why does man ignore the high cost of getting even, when his vengeful spirit may even cost him paralyzing strokes or fatal heart attacks?

One day a man came into my office with his fourteen-year-old boy. The father said to me, "I only came to get some more pills for my wife's colitis."

Immediately the youngster quipped, "Who was Ma colliding with this time?"

The woman's "colitis" is more properly termed irritable bowel syndrome or "IBS." IBS is the most common gastrointestinal disease in Western countries. It accounts for over half of all patient visits to medical specialists in intestinal disease. In one study, researchers found that three-fourths of these patients had psychiatric illnesses, such as depression and hysteria; and these diagnoses were often missed by their family doctor.[2] In fact, this diagnosis is so hard to make that abdominal cramps resulting from IBS are thought to be the most common cause for unnecessary surgery to remove the appendix. The basic underlying disorder seems to stem from hypersensitivity of the large intestinal (colonic) muscles to emotional stress. This hypersensitivity combined with an anxious or depressed personality will render a person truly miserable.

Is there any connection between this distressing disease—variably manifested as diarrhea, constipation, gas, or cramps—and our "colliding" with people and trying to get even?

Authorities now agree that the most common trigger of symptoms in IBS is a disordered reaction to emotional stress, such as fear, resentment, or anger. Flare-ups of IBS are often caused and perpetuated by "colliding" with others and attempting to get even.

For centuries scoffers have ridiculed the advice of Jesus to, "Love your enemies." They scorned it as impractical, idealistic, and absurd. Now psychiatrists have shown that this radical and life-changing attitude would prevent many of the ills man brings upon himself through resentment of his enemies.

The more serious ulcerative colitis also may be caused and aggravated by emotional turmoil. A current pathology text states that the first attack of bloody mucoid diarrhea is often "preceded by a stressful period in the patient's life."[3]

A medical doctor writes, "There are very significant emotional factors which influence not only the pathogenesis [causation] but also the course of the illness."[4] The ulcers in the colon can truly plague the sufferer, who often gets little help from any medication. Worse yet, "After 25 years of disease the risk [of colonic cancer] reaches the astounding rate of 40–50 percent."[5] The only surgical procedure of any avail is removal of the large intestine.

When Jesus said, "Forgive seventy-times seven," He was thinking not only of our souls, but of saving our bodies from irritable bowel syndrome, coronary artery disease, high blood pressure, and many other diseases.

Booker T. Washington, a man who was insulted times without number solely because of the color of his skin, wrote, "I will not let any man reduce my soul to the level of hatred."

The famous physiologist John Hunter knew what anger could do to his heart when he said, "The first scoundrel that gets me angry will kill me." Some time later, at a medical conference, a speaker made assertions that incensed Hunter. As he stood up and bitterly attacked the speaker, Hunter's anger caused such a violent contraction of his coronary arteries that he fell dead.

In life's frog ponds, we may be able to out croak our fellows, but it could truthfully be written on many millions of death certificates that the victims croaked from "irritable grudge syndrome."

We have heard people say, from between clenched teeth, "I'll get even with that skunk if it's the last thing I ever do!" Too often, they have foretold the truth.

A recent study surveyed 255 graduates of the University of North Carolina Medical School from the classes of 1954 to 1959. While in

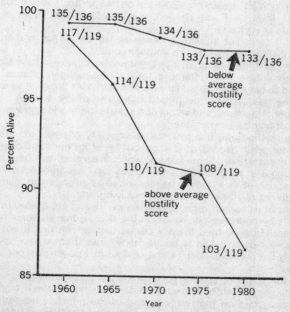

FIGURE 13: Differences in survival rates between men with below average and those with above average hostility scores.[6]

medical school, all of these physicians had taken a standard written test to determine their level of hostility. The preceding graph is taken from this study and it illustrates the enormous impact of hostile emotions on death and disease.

Those physicians who had above average levels of hostility died at a rate over six times greater than their fellow students who had more forgiving attitudes. These physicians, however, were an average of only fifty-one years old in 1981; and, judging from the shape of this graph, the difference between the number of survivors in each group will probably continue to increase.

The more "hostile" doctors in this study suffered five times as many heart attacks and were more likely to suffer from high blood pressure. They were no more likely to smoke, so this was not the cause of their high death and disease rate. These men are striking examples of the high cost of getting even.

I am reminded of a perky eighty-year-old lady who came to me at regular intervals to have her blood pressure checked. It usually hovered around an already high 200, but on one particular day it soared to 230. Inwardly I was startled; but I said, calmly, "Your blood pressure is up today."

With a smile she answered, "I can explain that. I just had an argument with Joe Syms in the waiting room."

Think of it: that cultured, intelligent woman could well have blown a cerebral fuse and suffered a fatal stroke, simply because she wanted to get even with a man well-known for his provocative chatter. She had correctly diagnosed the cause of her soaring blood pressure. Arguments and verbal duels cause many and aggravate all cases of high blood pressure.[7]

The methods we use to retaliate vary. My one-year-old granddaughter, when peeved, used to put out her little hands and claw the air in front of her. Some babies, when frustrated, will beat their heads against the floor. Because babies can't see their heads, it is the last part of their body to be recognized as belonging to them, so they do not realize whom they are really hurting.

Most of us cannot remember when we tried to get even with our parents by pounding our heads on the floor. However, some of us can recall how we tried to spite our parents by refusing to eat our meals. Our parents had to tell us many times that we were spiting nobody but ourselves, before that obvious fact penetrated our thick skulls.

In the space of several years, I treated three adolescents who tried to get even with their schoolmates by punching them. None of the youngsters on the receiving end of the punches needed any medical attention, but the three unskilled boxers suffered fractures of the bones in their hands.

A few years ago I knew a college student—we shall call him Pierre—who suffered a great deal from a burning pain in his upper belly. I gave him the newest, most-effective medication; but he obtained only partial and short-lived relief. Pierre went to several specialists but got no further relief. Extensive X ray studies revealed no problems. After observing his rather tense personality for several months, I felt that some emotional strain might be at the bottom of this trouble. Of course, he emphatically denied that he was under any tension.

Pierre was a puzzle until another student told me about hearing him speak in a nearby town. Pierre had devoted most of his speech to a harangue, describing how his grandfather had been wronged and defrauded several decades earlier. Pierre had stood rigid and had excoriated his family's enemies for over an hour while the perspiration streamed down his face. Not once did he stop to wipe his forehead. When he had finished, his voice was hoarse and his shirt soaked.

When Pierre came to my office the next time, I asked him again if he was suffering any mental strain or held any long-standing grudges against anyone. Again he denied any difficulties. Then I reminded him of the talk that had been reported to me. I suggested to him that his intense desire to get even with his grandfather's enemies was probably causing his stomach trouble. I used pictures to explain how emotional stress can increase the stomach's secretion of acid and enzymes. For the rest of his appointment he forgot about his stomach pains and badgered me to divulge the identity of the student who had given me the information, so that he could scold him for not "minding his own business."

Unfortunately, Pierre's desire for revenge was so intense that he refused to give up his resentments or seek further counseling. Paying the price with wretched days and sleepless nights, he fattened his many grudges by reciting them to every available listener.

Finally, Pierre's abdominal distress bothered him so much that he became unable to study or attend classes. He failed the next semester, and the academic dean was forced to dismiss him from the college.

Going up in the age scale, I recall a lawyer who, when bested in an argument with his wife, would try to get even with her by grinding his teeth together. It is still a mystery to me how he thought he was spiting her by grinding and tearing the fillings out of his own teeth. That wasn't even tooth for tooth!

Many chronological years separated this man from the baby who pounded her own head on the floor, yet in the area of interpersonal relationships he wasn't more mature than the cantankerous baby.

They acted similarly because they both possessed an innate carnal nature.

Most of us do not retaliate against others by pounding our heads on the floor or grinding our teeth together. Neither do we stab, poison, or shoot each other. The most common way we get even with others is by talking about them. That isn't scriptural either, but it has the advantage of keeping us clear of the electric chair.

Running people down exposes us to a host of diseases of body and mind. Expressing animosity toward others calls forth hormones from the pituitary, adrenal, thyroid, and other glands. In excess, these hormones can cause diseases in almost any part of the body.

I have found that the moment I start hating a man, I become his slave. I can't enjoy my work anymore because he even controls my thoughts. My resentments release excessive stress hormones and I become fatigued after only a few hours of work. The work I formerly enjoyed is now drudgery, and my brightly papered office seems like a dreary dungeon. Even vacations lose their pleasure. It may be a luxurious car that I drive along a lake fringed with the multicolored autumnal beauty of maple, oak, and birch; but moping in my resentment, I might as well be driving a hearse in mud and rain.

The man I hate hounds me wherever I go. I can't escape his tyrannical grasp on my mind. When the waiter serves me steamed lobster and clams, with asparagus, crisp salad, and strawberry shortcake smothered with ice cream, it might as well be stale bread and water. My teeth chew the food and I swallow it, but the man I hate will not allow me to enjoy it.

King Solomon must have had a similar experience, for he wrote: "Better a dish of vegetables with love, than the best beef served with hatred" (Proverbs 15:17 MOFFATT).

The man I hate may be many miles from my bedroom; but more cruel than any slave driver, he whips my thoughts into such a frenzy that my "perfect sleeper" mattress becomes a rack of torture. The lowliest of the serfs can sleep, but not I. I am, indeed, a slave to every man I hate.

Are we human beings less intelligent than grizzly bears? Why do we allow resentments to fill every moment in twenty-four hours with thoughts that fume like nitric acid and corrode as deeply? Why are we controlled far more than we want to admit by an inner force we jokingly accept as "Old Nick"?

I think Jesus gave the answer when James and John wanted Him to call down fire on a Samaritan village because the Samaritans wouldn't give them lodging. These disciples were believers in and followers of Jesus; yet, mind you, these Christians—controlled by the pride of religious and racial superiority—were so full of carnality that they besought the Lord to allow them to incinerate the village with "fire from heaven." The Lord rebuked them by saying, "You do not know what manner of spirit you are of" (Luke 9:55 NKJB-NT).

Before Pentecost, Peter also had an innate carnal spirit. In the Garden of Gethsemane, Peter, filled with a spirit of vengeance, tried to cut off the head of one of the opposition party. He wasn't the first or last carnal theologian who has retaliated by cutting off heads.

What a complete transformation occurred in James, John, and Peter after they crucified self and were filled with the Holy Spirit. The old spirit of getting even was replaced by the Holy Spirit of Christ— who, when He was reviled, reviled not in return.

The seventh chapter of Acts describes how Stephen, "being full of the Holy Spirit," reacted when he was stoned. He died a bloody and painful death—something similar to being dragged by the feet behind a slowly moving car; but Stephen was devoid of the spirit of revenge. Bleeding and bruised, he used his last bit of energy to get on his knees and pray, ". . . Lord, do not hold this sin against them . . ." (Acts 7:60 NIV). How many of us, stoned by a vicious mob of "stiff-necked . . . murderers" would be primarily interested in praying with our last breath for their spiritual welfare?

We can partly answer that question by taking a little inventory. Have we been engaged in hurling back the stones that have been thrown at us? Have we, in our conversations, been trying to cut off heads or call down fire upon those who have given us a rough time or even blasphemed against Christ? How have we reacted when one of our peers, either purposely or inadvertently, did something to annoy us? Did we slam the door, refuse to eat, sit and pout, or gossip about them? An honest appraisal should make it clear whether we are allowing God's Holy Spirit or Satan's carnal spirit to control our daily lives. Do Paul's words still haunt us: ". . . We died to sin; how can we live in it any longer?" (Romans 6:2 NIV).

Have you found yourself lacking? Christ does not intend for you to berate yourself, adding guilt to the sin of vengeance. On the contrary, John tells us, ". . . If anybody does sin, we have one who speaks to the Father in our defense—Jesus Christ, the Righteous One. He is the atoning sacrifice for our sins . . ." (1 John 2:1,2 NIV). We need not wallow as pigs in the mud of our guilt, for we can rejoice as saints in the joy of God's forgiveness.

Nevertheless, if we refuse to give up our resentments and do not allow His Spirit to control us, we will remain much more susceptible to many diseases of body and mind. We will continue to suffer from the eternally fatal disease of the soul—with which we were all born and of which we can only be cured by the forgiveness of God for our sin.

When the "natural man" is shamefully wronged, he can't resist the temptation to get even—even though it means paying the high price of his own health. However, if we who know the Lord drive His nails into everything in our lives contrary to His Word, Christ will crucify our carnal spirits.

Paul outlined the steps toward getting rid of the disease-producing spirit of retaliation:

> Put to death, therefore, whatever belongs to your
> earthly nature. . . . You used to walk in these
> ways, in the life you once lived; but off with
> them all now, off with anger, rage, malice,
> slander. . . . you have stripped off the old
> nature with its practices, and put on the new
> nature. . . . clothe yourselves with compassion,
> kindness, humility, gentleness and patience. Bear
> with each other and forgive whatever grievances you
> may have against one another. Forgive as the
> Lord forgave you. And over all these virtues put
> on love, which binds them all together in perfect
> unity.
>
> Colossians 3:5,7–10,12–14[8]

"None of these diseases" is the promise available to us only if we "have stripped off the old nature with its practices" of getting even.

Chapter Twelve

Eggs—Just Eggs

"Doctor, my wife and I have driven thirty miles to talk to you. We hardly ever get sick. But for the last few months we haven't been able to sleep at night. We've been taking sleeping pills, sometimes two or more a night, but we still can't sleep. I began to develop pains in the pit of my stomach. Dr. Lorah took an X ray, but he said it looked fine. My wife started to have pains over her heart, but Dr. Edmunds examined her and said there wasn't anything physically wrong with her. We drove over here this afternoon to see if you could help us."

They were a pleasant-looking couple in their early seventies who had recently retired from teaching school. I had never seen them before. I was very busy that afternoon, and they had already been examined by two thoroughly competent doctors—so I was puzzled about how to help them in the short time at my disposal.

After I asked the woman a few questions and made a superficial examination without finding an obvious problem, she pulled a letter out of her pocket. "Doctor, you may think I am foolish; but our troubles seemed to start right after we got this letter."

Dear George,
I understand that you are selling some eggs to Harry Bickerstaff. You know that I have invested considerable

money in the chicken business and can supply more eggs
to the people of this little hamlet than they can eat. You
ought to know that my business is hurt by your dabbling
around with a few hens and selling eggs to Harry. I think
you ought to stop.

MANNING CASPAR

Her eyes were wet with tears when I looked up at her. She continued, "We felt we had a right to sell those eggs to Harry because he
preferred our Rhode Island brown eggs to the white ones. But now,
Manning Caspar refuses to speak to either one of us when we see
him on the street. We feel terrible because we never had an experience like this. We have been upset over the whole matter. I think our
whole trouble stems from eggs—just eggs."

When she suggested that they go home and give up their egg
business, I agreed and told her it might be worth a try. Several
months later the couple's daughter told me they had done just that,
and they had never felt better. They had stopped taking sleeping
capsules, and their aches and pains had ceased.

Of course, they had a perfect right to continue to sell eggs. Perhaps it was a foolish thing for them to give in to Manning Caspar. Or
was it? They had already spent close to $200 for X rays and other
examinations, while their total profits from the egg business
amounted to only a few dollars. In dollars and cents it wasn't a paying business. Besides, they had lost their peace of mind, the value of
which is priceless.

I once heard a story about a man who was surprised to discover
that a minister had given up his pulpit several years before and was
practicing medicine. This man asked the doctor why he had done it.
"I took up the practice of medicine because I discovered that people
will pay more money to care for their bodies than for their souls," he
answered.

Some years later he gave up medicine and became an attorney.
Perplexed, his friend again asked for a reason. "I took up the practice of law because I discovered that people will pay more money to
get their own way than for either body or soul."

How right he was! Countless people today are ruining body, mind,
and soul because they insist on having their own selfish ways.
Worthwhile is the saying "A man is a fool who can't be angry, but a
man is wise who won't be angry."

The retired couple were cured of unhappiness, insomnia, and
disease—because they put the admonitions of the Bible ahead of
their own right to sell eggs: "If someone forces you to go one mile,
go with him two miles" (Matthew 5:41 NIV). Foolish advice? To walk
an extra mile and insure peace of mind and unbroken sleep night

after night? Any of us who have done it can testify to the refreshing medical benefits we have experienced in our own bodies. Jesus, in giving this command, must have been thinking of our bodies and minds as well as our souls. "And if someone wants to sue you and take your tunic, let him have your cloak as well" (Matthew 5:40 NIV).

Our pride suffers from such a course, but we gain improved health and sustained happiness. God isn't the ogre that some make Him out to be; His commandments are for our own good.

Will we cater to our health or to our pride? Will we obey or disobey the Lord. Each of us makes this decision every day of our lives.

Love or Perish

 An astounding number of carnal attitudes and emotions can lead to psychosomatic illnesses. These feelings are not new to our generation. In fact, they were carefully catalogued by the Apostle Paul almost two thousand years ago. In 1 Corinthians 13, Paul listed these attitudes and prescribed their antidote—love.

Paul, however, was not talking about that gushy feeling when you know that "this time it's really, really real. This time it's really going to last." Paul was discussing the attitude that the King James Version translated with the word *charity*—that type of love that embodies the biblical command, "Nobody should seek his own good, but the good of others" (1 Corinthians 10:24 NIV).

On the next page, I have broken up Paul's definition of love into its various elements. To the right of each element, I have listed various corresponding disease-causing emotions, extracted directly from a psychiatry textbook by Dr. Lawrence Kolb.[1]

The devil, as a snake, has injected every man with his venom; and love is the only antidote that can save us from these poisonous attitudes. Psychiatrist Smiley Blanton emphasized this fact in the title of one of his books, *Love or Perish*. Without love—that thoughtfulness and keen consideration of others—we become much more likely to perish from a variety of diseases of mind and body.

An internationally known psychiatrist, Alfred Adler, writes, "The

LOVE	Attitudes that produce disease
is patient	frustration
	discontent
is kind	aggressiveness
does not envy	envy
	jealousy
does not boast	seeking attention
is not proud	overvalued body concept
is not rude	taking attitude
is not self-seeking	selfishness
	greed
is not easily angered	anger
	rage
	irritableness
keeps no record of wrongs	resentment
	hatred
does not delight in evil	death wishes for others
	sexual fantasizing
rejoices with the truth	dejection
	depression
always protects	competitiveness
always trusts	anxiety
	doubt
	striving for security
	paranoia
always hopes	fear
	despair
	discouragement
always perseveres	irresponsibility
	apathy

most important task imposed by religion has always been, 'Love thy neighbor. . . .' It is the individual who is not interested in his fellow man who has the greatest difficulties in life and provides the greatest injury to others. It is from among such individuals that all human failures spring."[2] Dr. Adler based these sweeping conclusions on a careful analysis of thousands of patients. He held that a lack of love was responsible for "all human failures."

This should not surprise students of the Scriptures, for love was the granite building block on which God built his covenant with Israel. Finding love too difficult to maintain, Israel dislodged this stone and replaced it with a conglomerate of smug legalism. When Jesus came to earth, however, He built a new covenant, using the same old cornerstone—love—that was the cornerstone of God's covenant with Israel. He reaffirmed God's greatest commandment as, " 'Love the Lord your God with all your heart and with all your soul and with all your mind.' This is the first and greatest commandment. And the second is like it: 'Love your neighbor as yourself.' All the Law and the Prophets hang on these two commandments" (Matthew 22:37–40 NIV).

History shows us that when the nation of Israel failed to live by the commandments of God, they failed in everything they did. When they failed to follow God's commandment to love, interminable famines killed thousands; foreign nations decimated the land; and—worst of all—an unloving Israel rejected her Messiah. Israel is an object lesson on the result of disobeying God—failure.

When I quote the Bible and Dr. Adler to patients who are suffering physically and mentally from a lack of love, some of them retort that it is very difficult to change one's feelings—to change hate to love. That is true. Psychologists support this view, for we, as humans, cannot gain complete control over our feelings.

However, psychologists also state that our wills can control our actions. What we *will* to do is usually what we will do. Our wills can give us freedom from bondage to our fickle emotions.

Can a person freely choose to do something that he does not feel like doing? Yes, he can. But to do so he must consider some code or ethic to be more important than his own feelings. Our culture says, "If it feels good, do it." But this is no answer, for it enslaves us to our emotions.

Jesus summarized the code of the New Covenant—this code by which a Christian must live: "Love your enemies, bless those who curse you, do good to those who hate you" (Luke 6:35 NKJB-NT). Do something good for your enemy, and you will be surprised to find how much easier it is to love him. Not only does following Christ's teachings set us free from our emotions, it actually transforms our sinful emotions. We can then become slaves to love. Yet, not slaves; for slavery to love is unsurpassed liberation.

No longer should we say, "If it feels good, do it." We must live by the motto, "If Christ commands it, do it." A Christian must live no other way. As John wrote, "We know that we have come to know him [Christ] if we obey his commands" (1 John 2:3 NIV).

Christ commands us to do good to all men—even our enemies. This is the scripturally and psychologically sound method for transforming carnal attitudes into loving attitudes.

"Do good to them that hate you." Impossible? Not if you follow some easy directions. The first step in performing the impossible is to walk out into your kitchen. Now, you *can* do that.

Step number two! Make up a lemon meringue pie as delicious as one on a magazine cover. Or make a pecan pie if that is your forte. Actually the kind isn't too important as long as you dress up that pie as though it were going on exhibition. You have made your pie. So far so good! By now you have begun to feel a little better.

Sternly look at your feet, and forcefully inform them, "Feet, you are going to carry me and this pie to Mrs. Quirk's. Yes, I know you haven't even seen her home in many years, but you are going there today."

Off you go. As you begin your adventure to seek the golden fleece of love, you feel a strange transformation——a warming, deep in the left side of your chest. Inside you feel the same anticipation as when you sighted icicles melting in the April sun.

Across the railroad tracks and down the dingy alley called Depot Street——you begin to understand Mrs. Quirk's attitude a little better as the roar from a freight train shakes dilapidated houses, as the black soot from the overhead tracks soils your white coat, and as dirty children in the streets scream filthy obscenities.

"Yes," you say to yourself, "if I had to live here, I think I would be irritable too."

As you go up the steps, you cannot help smiling at the vastly new role you are playing. You rap on the door and wait. To Mrs. Quirk's truly surprised look, you present your peace offering with a smile that surprises even you.

A little chat in the living room, a cordial invitation for her to visit your home, and as you leave, a mutual hug and kiss. The fervor and spontaneity of it surprises both of you. The love of God is truly coursing through your whole being. The impossible has happened!

On your way home you feel like skipping along the street, as you did when you were a carefree girl. You wonder where this feeling of complete freedom, forgotten with youth, had been hiding. The spirit of rejoicing, of singing, and of dancing have shattered the shackles of hatred. What a metamorphosis! What a miracle!

You feel so good that you decide not to stop at the doctor's office to take that shot for your frayed nerves. They aren't frayed any- more. You never felt better——even the pain in your back is gone.

> He drew a circle that shut me out——
> Heretic, rebel, a thing to flout.
> But love and I had the wit to win:
> We drew a circle that took him in.[3]

"Love your enemies, do good to them that hate you." That may be a very bitter tonic to swallow; but you will discover that when it reaches the heart, it will be surprisingly invigorating, exhilarating, and liberating. You can love; you need not perish. By doing good, you can change hate to love.

Chapter Fourteen

Cats and Crocodiles

 When a cat unexpectedly encounters a dog, the hairs on the cat's back stand on end. Its heartbeat surges, blood pressure soars, and breathing rate accelerates. Adrenaline and other glandular products are immediately squirted into the bloodstream because the emotional centers, aroused by fear, send lightning-quick messages of alarm to all parts of the body. The body's response to these messages is called the *fight or flight reaction.*

A close relative to the cat is the lion, which we have often seen in the zoo. In his cage he restlessly paces back and forth hundreds of times a day. He is fearful, fidgety, and frustrated. When he stops a moment to peer through the bars, his expression is anxious and there are deep vertical furrows in his forehead—the exact brow and image of a man who is filling out his annual income-tax return.

In another part of the zoo is the crocodile, quite a contrast to the lion. Mr. Crocodile lies there, motionless as an old log; he rarely even blinks his eyes. He is the animalization of tranquility. He certainly doesn't worry about what the Lyons might say about him; neither is he trying to keep up with the Barrs. Of bumps and blemishes on his face he has plenty, but he has never shed any crocodile tears over them.

How long do these two different animals live? In one zoo, I saw a lion that was twenty-five-years old. His eyes were dim and his gait was unsteady. He was truly decrepit and sorely in need of dentures. At only twenty-five he was ready for the boneyard.

Is the crocodile old at twenty-five? Not at all! He lives long after the bones of the lion are dried and bleached.

Why do these two animals have such vastly different life spans? Dr. George Crile gave a group of doctors a reasonable answer in his Cleveland Clinic Museum. He had mounted many stuffed animals from all over the world, and by the side of each animal were exact replicas of its adrenal and thyroid glands.

The lion had very large adrenal glands. He had lived a life of great stress with frequent alarm reactions. The lion's emotional centers were ever calling for plenty of adrenaline (secreted by the *adrenal* gland) for his fierce fights with other lions or swift flights after water buffalo. The lion had a large thyroid gland, indicating that he had packed the hours with strenuous activity.

In marked contrast, these same glands in the crocodile were very small. His emotional centers had not been making rapid demands for their products, and adrenaline had not repeatedly whipped his heart to full-throttle speed. Nor had adrenaline been raising his blood pressure and prematurely hardening his arteries.

In a human being, the number of alarms sent out from the emotional centers also influences the size of stress glands such as the

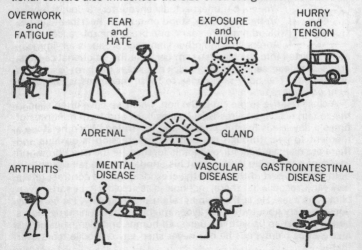

FIGURE 14: Stressors and Diseases.[1]

adrenal and thyroid. The New York State Department of Health published photographs of two human adrenal glands. One gland was normal in size, the other greatly enlarged—"a result of stress."[2] The individual from whom the enlarged gland was removed probably died many years ahead of his time because the increased supply of adrenaline played havoc with one or more of his bodily functions. He not only shortened his days, but his days were likely filled with emotional turmoil.

We must also take note, however, that the adrenal glands are normally necessary and beneficial. If you awake at night to the fact that a burglar has broken into your house, fear arouses emotional centers in your brain causing definite chemical changes within the brain itself. The brain then sends out messages to the adrenal glands. An increased supply of their hormones, adrenaline and cortisol, enables your heart to beat faster and mobilizes sugars from your liver, giving more energy for either a fight or a flight.

This reserve of energy can be lifesaving if one is running from a lion or crossing a busy highway. But, if a person sits at high noon in the security of his own home and, instead of relaxing, allows his mind to think of burglars or of the man who is out to destroy his business, then his emotional centers will send out alarm messages to the glands, heart, and blood-pressure centers—just as if an individual were actually attacking him. Although the body needs an excess of hormones for genuine emergency situations, an excessive and frequent production of hormones over weeks and months results in harmful effects.

In the past few decades, psychiatrists have begun to recognize this potentially lethal behavior. They have labeled this type of personality, "type A." About 40 percent of the American population exhibit this personality. There are four basic traits that distinguish the type A personality: "time-consciousness or hurry-sickness; extremes in competition; a tendency to use other people to achieve personal goals; and an inner hostility."[3]

Hurry-sickness is best exemplified by the person who can never relax. Each day, he tries to do his work faster. A type A surgeon once passed David on the stairs in a hospital. As he bumped him out of the way, the surgeon offered David what he thought to be very good advice, "You'll never get to be a good surgeon, if you don't even run the stairs."

A type A person always has to be on the move. In fact, he avoids relaxation in any way he can. If his wife wants to sit and talk, he excuses himself to go do some work that he brought from the office. If he has to wait in line, he gets very restless.

Frantic efforts toward unreachable and ill-defined goals force him to live like Sisyphus, the legendary king of Corinth whose punishment in hell was to push a huge boulder up a hill. Each time he neared the summit, the boulder would roll back down the hill. For eternity, Sisyphus continued in frustration, never experiencing the elation of accomplishment and never able to rest and contemplate his labor.

Dr. Ulf Lundberg did an interesting experiment where he compared intense (type A) personalities with the more "laid back" (type B) personalities. While they were allowed to work, both groups had similar stress-hormone levels, heart rates and "self-reported discomfort." However, when they were forced to rest, type A persons, in comparison with type B persons, had higher levels of adrenaline and cortisol, higher heart rates, and they reported twice as much discomfort. What irony: they found rest to be stressful![4]

The competitiveness of the type A person pervades all of his relationships. He competes against his business associates. He competes against his wife. He even competes against his children. He is obsessed with "moving up" in his company; or, if he is the head of his company, he is obsessed with making his company the biggest and the best. His wife "can never drive the car as well" as he can, so riding in the car while she drives makes him very anxious for his safety. He is sure and often informs his son that the young lad does not play baseball as well as he did.

A type A person uses others. In personal relationships, he only associates with another person if that person helps him reach his own selfish goals. His wife is "good for" him. She gives him an "aura of respectability." She can do the housework and take care of the kids: jobs that he "doesn't have time to do."

His inner feeling of hostility is due to his constant pursuit of unreachable goals. Anyone or anything that hinders him in his current flurry of activity becomes an object of his wrath. Type A people often have quick tempers; but they think that this helps them, because people are "not as likely to get in the way once they know what the consequences are."

The type A person often excuses his behavior as necessary to "get to the top of the heap." This excuse may seem to make sense; after all, "you have to fight to get to the top." But where in the Bible are Christians told to aspire to greatness or wealth? Jesus said, "Do not worry about your life . . . but seek first the kingdom of God and His righteousness, and all these things shall be added to you" (Matthew 6:25,33 NKJB-NT). Not surprisingly, scientific studies have found no association between type A behavior and occupational position. In fact, some experts in the field feel that type A behavior actually hinders success.[5]

Type A behavior has been associated with coronary artery disease in many scientific studies. In fact, many experts refer to this personality as the "coronary prone" personality. In one study, doctors injected dye into their patients' coronary arteries and then took X rays of these arteries. Type A patients made up an astounding 82 percent of those patients with arteries that were over three-quarters clogged. They also made up 63 percent of the patients with lesser disease. Thus, type A behavior has been proven to lead to serious physical disease.

But physical disease is not the most serious consequence of type A behavior. Cardiologist Dr. Jay Hollman wrote an article entitled, "Type A Behavior is a Spiritual Disease."[6] In this article, Dr. Hollman describes the effects of this serious spiritual disease:

> Constantly pushing himself to go faster, he loses the joy of relaxation. . . . After competing with people and using people, he loses the joy of friendship and relationship. . . . Frantic effort to achieve an impossible goal . . . often results in much wasted effort through incomplete projects or projects done poorly and uncreatively because of an obsession to finish. This usually robs the type A person of any joy associated with the project. . . . Value on detail (rather than the bigger goal) leads him to frantic purposelessness. . . .
>
> [He] must put down another in order that [he himself] may be greater. . . . Deep at the roots of such behavior is a despicable type of selfishness that allows [him] to think that his goals, ideas or plans are more important than others.[7]

Yes, type A behavior is a "spiritual disease." It is a disease that is constantly encouraged by our society. We are bombarded with advertisements that glorify hurry: witness the recent television ads for overnight mail. "He's a tremendously fast worker" is often a higher compliment than "He does good work."

Although these personality patterns are thoroughly ingrained in type A persons, their situation is not hopeless. After defining the seriousness of this spiritual disease, Dr. Hollman prescribes corrective measures necessary for each type A personality trait.[8] I have summarized his prescription:

1. *To cure hurry-sickness:* Make it your daily practice to " 'Be still and know that I am God.' Set achievable goals and accomplish them."
2. *To cure competitiveness:* Refuse to compare yourself with other people. Learn to rejoice when others (even your opponents) succeed.

3. *To cure selfish use of others:* Give yourself to others without expecting anything in return. Consider people more important than plans.
4. *To cure hostility:* Refuse (unless absolutely necessary) to engage in any work or recreation that you despise. And, most importantly, trust God—even when every-one seems to be out to get you—and He will give you that inner peace that "passeth understanding."

Recently, David heard a popular evangelist on television who bragged about how hard he worked—claiming that his work was his "recreation." He said that golf would be a fine game "if you could play it in a half hour." His work took up so much time that he could only afford "four hours a night" for sleep.

His enthusiasm may have inspired many of his listeners, but his words saddened us. He was too busy. Not only could his obsessive behavior lead to the untimely death of a man used of God, it was outward evidence that this man, who was responsible for the spir-itual well-being of so many thousands, could be heading for burn-out. What made his spiritual condition even more tragic was the fact that he did not recognize his problem. He actually thought that it was an asset. Hard work is often necessary; but this type of attitude toward any job, even "the Lord's work," inevitably results in spir-itual wasting.

When Jesus told the parable of the sower, he talked of the seed that fell among thorns. The thorns deprived the seed of nutrients from the soil, so the plants did not mature and never bore fruit. Such is the plight of type A people: ". . . who hear [the word], but as they go on their way they are choked by life's worries . . . and they do not mature" (Luke 8:14 NIV).

Solomon knew of this problem when he wrote, ". . . the man in a hurry misses the way" (Proverbs 19:2 NEB). A man in a hurry may look as though he is doing much, but he accomplishes little; for in his rushing, he is unable to spend time meditating and seeking God's direction. He may "go far"; but where has he gone?

Living like the lion—constantly chasing and fighting—exposes a person to dangerous levels of hormones and sinful attitudes. No man can live victoriously until he takes on the nature of a crocodile and practices the admonition of the psalmist, David: "Be still before the Lord and wait patiently for him . . ." (Psalms 37:7 NIV). If we do not make this our daily practice we will, surely, "miss the way" to spiritual and physical health.

Chapter Fifteen

Arthritis From a Panther Scare

 A farmer about forty-five years old came into my office some time ago. I noticed that his fingers on both hands were badly deformed with rheumatoid arthritis, and I asked him how long he had suffered from this debilitating disease.

"Ever since I was nine years old," he replied. "You see, rumor had it that there was a panther on the loose in the neighborhood. Walking to and from school, I had to go through a stretch of thick woods. Every time I got to those woods, I ran as fast as I could and never looked back. I was scared stiff that the panther would jump me. In a couple weeks, my hands looked like this. They've been deformed ever since."

Does this sound strange? How could emotional stress lead to this severely disabling disease? Nobody knows how; but research has repeatedly shown that the rheumatoid arthritis that begins in children is definitely associated with stressful periods in these children's lives. This disease cripples more childen than any other musculoskeletal disease, even more than muscular dystrophy, and is a major cause of childhood blindness.

Researchers have carefully documented stressful events in the lives of children during the year before they came down with the disease. Each event was assigned a certain number of "Life Change

135

Units" or LCU's: for example—death of a parent counted for about 90 LCU's; moving to a new school district counted for about 50 LCU's; and an increase in number of arguments between parents counted for about 47 LCU's. When all these points were added up, children with rheumatoid arthritis had an average life-change score of 177 for the year before they came down with the disease; healthy children had an average score of only 83. Thus, during the year preceding the onset of disease, these arthritic children had suffered, in the form of drastic life changes, more than twice the normal stress for children of that age.[1]

Studies have also linked the development of the more common adult-onset rheumatoid arthritis to emotional upset. Two experts in the field state, "It is now evident that the development of rheumatoid arthritis is dependent both on blood abnormalities and emotional stress."[2]

A specific chemical, rheumatoid factor, is found in the blood of about 70 percent of patients with rheumatoid arthritis. For every patient with rheumatoid arthritis, however, there are two people who carry rheumatoid factor in their blood but have no arthritis. Researchers have studied relatives of patients with rheumatoid arthritis. They found that relatives who had rheumatoid factor but no arthritis felt much less guilt, loneliness, fear, lack of control, and low self-esteem. This research seems to demonstrate that "Given a genetic or constitutional predisposition to rheumatoid disease, individuals with significant emotional conflict and psychological distress go on to the development of disease."[3]

Dr. Loring Swaim, former president of the American Rheumatism Association, observed that emotional factors are often crucial in producing rheumatoid arthritis. He noticed that unhappy events and long periods of sustained emotional strain almost always preceded the first painful attack of arthritis. During his many years in practice, Dr. Swaim witnessed many miraculous cures and remissions in his patients due to faith in God. Although we must not dismiss the possibility that God miraculously intervened into the joints of these patients, it seems likely that these cures were due to God's miraculously intervening into their souls. He offered forgiveness for their guilt, comfort in their loneliness, freedom from their fears, control over their lives, and assurance of their self-worth. In short, faith in God removed the emotions that scientists have specifically linked to rheumatoid arthritis.[4]

Many a man fears the loss of an acre of his farm or even a few inches of a city lot because of the claims of his neighbor. Surveyors give conflicting opinions. He will not rest until the court makes its decision. Foolish and impractical seem the words of Jesus to a man in this situation: "If anyone wants to sue you and take away your tunic, let him have your cloak also" (Matthew 5:40 NKJB-NT). The disturbed man considers Jesus' advice idealistic and ill suited to a twentieth-century problem. Instead, he decides to fight it out in the courts and hires a lawyer.

During the long months before his case is called, the tense days of the trial, and the months after the trial—his pituitary, adrenal, and thyroid glands work overtime, pumping their products into his system. When the judge finally hands down the decision—his neighbor takes the man's shirt, his lawyer takes his coat, and the court costs take his trousers. All too often such a man ends up in a wheelchair for the rest of his life, with disabling arthritis or some other disease—a high price to pay for rejecting the Lord's advice.

Any discussion of the effect of fear on the body would not be complete without considering the effect of this emotion on the heart. I recall the case of a prominent Israeli physician who was reading a newspaper account of the murderous persecution of Jews in Russia, where many of his relatives lived. To a friend in the room he mentioned the great fear he felt for the safety of his loved ones. A moment later he slumped over dead in his chair, a victim of a clot of the coronary artery (the artery that supplies the heart with blood).

Can psychic stress really precipitate occlusion of the coronary artery—the most common killer in America? A number of recent medical articles have emphasized the importance of stress in this condition. Although there are many other factors important in setting the stage for coronary-artery disease—such as eating saturated fats, eating excess calories, and smoking tobacco products—stress also seems to play a very important part.

Many studies indicate that people who die of heart attacks have suffered a time of increased stress in their lives. Researchers interviewed the spouses of patients who had died suddenly from heart attacks. These spouses recalled the stressful events in their mates' lives during the two years preceding their deaths. The researchers rated these stressful events on a "Life Change Unit" (LCU) scale of severity; for example, troubles with in-laws rated 22 LCU's, getting fired from work rated 50 LCU's, and death of a spouse rated 105 LCU's. People who died suddenly of heart attacks had suffered increasingly severe stress during the months preceding their fatal attacks.

Figure 15 illustrates the cataclysmic buildup of stress before a fatal heart attack. At the far right side of the graph we see that all 119 of the patients died suddenly from coronary heart disease. All these patients had been in good health until they unexpectedly died of heart attacks. During each quarter of the year preceding their fatal attacks, these men suffered increasingly stressful events, until their average stress level peaked at two to three times the level of

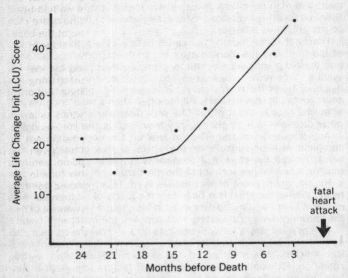

FIGURE 15: Life Change Unit buildup (as recorded by next of kin) for previously healthy patients who died suddenly of coronary heart disease.[5]

the previous year. Within three months of this stress peak, their hearts could no longer cope with the stresses of life, so they escaped from these stresses altogether.

When we experience "stressful events" in our lives, however, we need not suffer unduly from them. Consider the stress that my wife once experienced on our Canadian fishing trip. My wife, my daughter, and I arrived at Matawan, Ontario, about five o'clock on a Saturday evening. We wanted to catch some fish for our Sunday meals, so my daughter, Linda, and I rowed a boat up the treacherous Matawan Rapids, which was new territory to us. My wife stayed in the cabin to unpack and arrange things for the night. Then she sat down to await our return. Eight o'clock passed, but no boat came down the swiftly moving river. Then nine o'clock, nine-thirty——still no daughter, no husband appeared.

Fishing at that time of night was foolish and dangerous; but if my wife had become hysterical from worry, the internal stress would have made the situation seem even more gloomy and would have inflicted damage on her own body. In her time of need, however, the Lord reminded her of Psalms 34:4 from the passage we had been memorizing on our vacation: "I sought the Lord, and he heard me, and delivered me from all my fears" (KJV). My wife sought the Lord, and He truly did deliver her from all her fears as she sat alone in the darkness, the lantern by her side.

At ten o'clock she heard the voice of Linda behind her on the shore: "Daddy sent me by land, because he didn't want to bring me down the rapids in the dark. The fish were slow in biting; but once they started, they bit like a house afire!"

Still more waiting. Ten-thirty, and no boat. To my wife's calls, no answer came from the dark, swirling river. She knew she was doing everything she could by praying fervently and keeping the lantern on the dock. She had ample reason to fear, but the Lord had given her that peace of mind that passeth understanding. She did not panic or start off with the lantern to search for help. Instead, her faith in the scriptural promise, a promise that the Lord had tailored for this special need, gave her restful assurance. Divine strength she needed, since it was not until eleven o'clock that the evidence of her faith arrived safely at the dock.

Chapter Sixteen

You're As Old As Your Arteries

 While we run life's gauntlet of many killers, modern medical science can often come to our aid. Doctors can often eliminate Mr. Cancer with surgery, radiation, and chemotherapy. They can control Mr. Diabetes with a few squirts of insulin. They can even liquidate Mr. Pneumonia with a "shot" of penicillin.

But successfully defying medical weapons, Mr. Arteriosclerosis still strikes down four out of every ten gauntlet runners.

Bad arteries are the basic cause of cerebral strokes, heart attacks, angina pectoris, intestinal gangrene, certain kidney diseases, as well as other fatal conditions. Since arteriosclerotic arteries cause such widespread trouble, it is not surprising that so many people die from this common condition. Living tissue requires blood, so serious disease and death follow quickly when blockage of a tubular artery cuts off the blood supply to a vital organ, such as the heart or brain. If these arteries could only be kept open, almost half of the people who now die would go on living.

Over 40 million Americans suffer from one or more forms of heart or blood-vessel disease. As many as 1.5 million Americans have heart attacks each year, and over one-third of them die. The health-care costs for cardiovascular disease alone amount to over $40 billion. Arteriosclerosis can truthfully be called "everyone's disease."

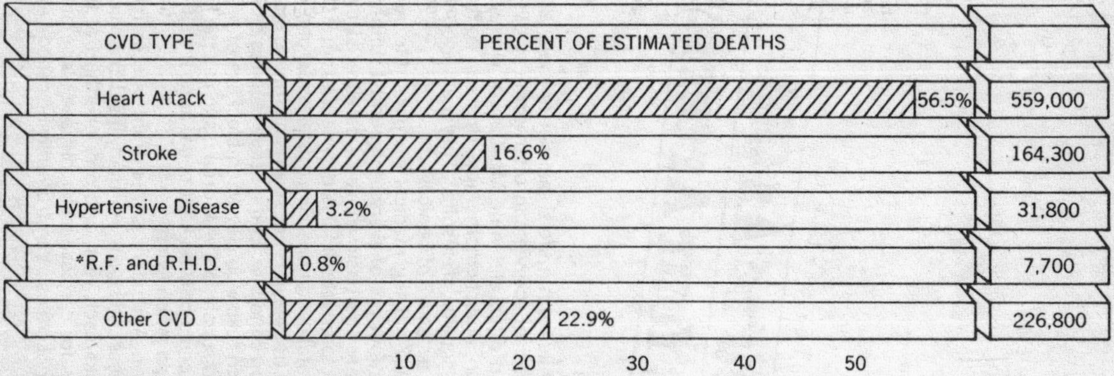
CVD TYPE
PERCENT OF ESTIMATED DEATHS
Heart Attack
56.5%
559,000
Stroke
16.6%
164,300
Hypertensive Disease
3.2%
31,800
*R.F. and R.H.D.
0.8%
7,700
Other CVD
22.9%
226,800
10
20
30
40
50

* Rheumatic Fever and Rheumatic Heart Disease
Source: National Center for Health Statistics, U.S. Public Health Service, DHHS

FIGURE 16: Estimated deaths in USA for 1981 due to cardiovascular diseases by major type of disorder.[1]

Development of Atherosclerosis

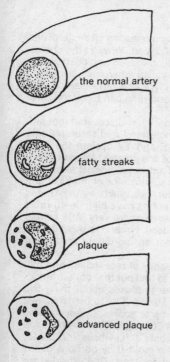

the normal artery

fatty streaks

plaque

advanced plaque

Heart Attack
(shaded area of
heart muscle dies)

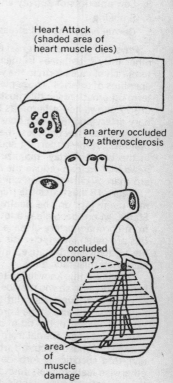

an artery occluded
by atherosclerosis

occluded
coronary

area
of
muscle
damage

FIGURE 17: Buildup of atheroma in coronary artery, resulting in a heart attack.[2]

Scientists have discovered that many factors increase the risk of death from this great killer. The most important of these include:

1. Eating saturated fats and cholesterol
2. Obesity
3. Low amounts of activity and exercise
4. Smoking
5. Carnal emotions and stress

Physicians now place great emphasis on reducing cholesterol and other fatty substances in their patients' blood. Why? Fatty, choles-terol-rich plaques form in the walls of blood vessels and obstruct the openings of arteries. These plaques are called atheromas, hence the term atherosclerosis: the most common type of arteriosclerosis. Fig-ure 17 shows how atheromas build up and then can block the coro-nary artery and lead to a heart attack.

In the past few decades, medical science has discovered that ani-mal fats are an important source of cholesterol and saturated fats in the blood. Today, magazines, radio, and TV declare the good news that we can reduce the ravages of the greatest killer of West-ern man by cutting down our intake of saturated animal fats.

Figure 18 illustrates the tremendous significance of intake of ani-mal meat fats on the death rate. Countries, such as the United States, where people eat a lot of animal fats have high death rates from coronary-artery disease. In countries where very little animal fats are eaten, athersclerosis is rare indeed. Finland is skewed from the straight line because Finlanders eat an inordinate amount of saturated milk fats.

Obtaining this knowledge took thousands of researchers and mil-lions of dollars, so you may be amazed to find out that our ultramod-ern research supports what God spoke to Moses about thirty-five hundred years ago: "The Lord said to Moses, 'Say to the Israelites: "Do not eat any of the fat of cattle, sheep or goats. . . . Anyone who eats the fat of an animal from which an offering by fire may be made to the Lord must be cut off from his people' " (Leviticus 7:22,23,25 NIV). God specifically forbade eating the most fatty portions of the otherwise lean animals found in Palestine. Thus, God provided for the protection of His people against arteriosclerosis.

Obesity is another important factor in the formation of choles-terol plaques within the arteries. Anyone more than 20 percent overweight is at a much greater risk for atheroscerosis and is, there-fore, classified as obese. Obesity stands, unrivaled, as the most common nutritional disorder in the civilized world. About one third of American adults and adolescents are obese—an epidemic, if there ever was one.

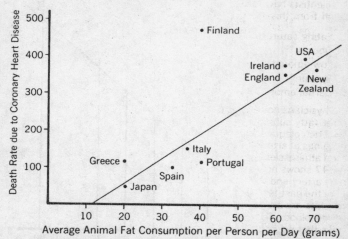

FIGURE 18: Coronary heart disease deaths plotted against average consumption of animal meat fats in different countries.[3]

Since this extra weight is composed of fat, the obese already have plenty of animal fat under their own skins. Obese persons, also, are prone to high blood pressure, high blood lipids, and high blood sugar (diabetes)—all of which result in increased atherosclerosis.

If every American were at optimum weight, we would see an astounding decrease in disease. Coronary heart disease would decrease 25 percent; strokes and heart failure would plummet over 30 percent.[4] Dr. W. B. Kannel has said, "Correction of overweight is probably the most important hygienic measure (aside from avoidance of cigarettes) available for the control of cardiovascular disease [arteriosclerosis]."[5]

The Bible has many warnings against intemperate eating habits. Many times gluttons and drunkards are mentioned in the same verse. One such verse says: "Do not join those who drink too much wine or gorge themselves on meat" (Proverbs 23:20 NIV). Christians have been among the first to condemn alcoholic beverages, but I have seldom heard sermons addressed to the sin of gluttony. Although this sin is common among members of almost every church in the land, most preachers—especially those who wish to keep their positions beyond the current year—continue to ignore the biblical injunctions against overeating. For millions of Christians, how-

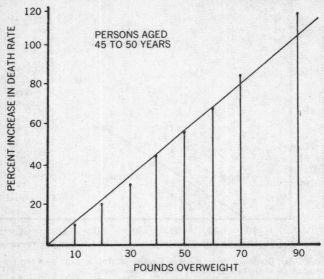

Pounds overweight	Increase in death rate over average, %
10	8
20	18
30	28
40	45
50	56
60	67
70	81
90	116

FIGURE 19: Relationship between increased obesity and increased death rate.

ever, obedience to these biblical warnings would fortify character, improve appearance, revive happiness, renew efficiency, restore health, and increase longevity.

After God created Adam, He ". . . put him in the Garden of Eden to work it and take care of it" (Genesis 2:15 NIV). God's original plan for man, even a man in a garden of paradise, included manual labor. When He commanded Israel to keep the Sabbath, he did not say, "Take every Saturday off"; but He reaffirmed this plan, "Six days you shall labor and do all your work" (Exodus 20:9 NIV).

A tragedy of modern society is that many jobs within the labor force require little physical exertion. However, people who work in jobs that require physical exertion, such as farming and dock work, have a much lower death rate due to atherosclerosis. Daily physical exertion protects against atherosclerosis in at least four ways:

1. It increases a helpful type of cholesterol in the blood that blocks deposition of harmful cholesterol.
2. It increases blood supply to the heart so that the heart is not damaged as seriously if a single artery is blocked.
3. It burns up fat and decreases obesity.
4. It produces a sense of well-being.

Paul taught: "Bodily exercise profits a little, but godliness is profitable for all things . . ." (1 Timothy 4:8 NKJB-NT). Some Christians mistake this verse to mean that exercise is a waste of time. By comparing physical exercise to physical food, we can see the fallacy in this reasoning. Although Jesus taught that spiritual food was of more value than physical food (John 6:30–59), he never taught that men should neglect proper eating. In the same way, spiritual exercise (fasting, praying, and so forth) is more important than physical exercise, but that does not mean that we should neglect physical exercise.

Proper exercise is especially important for today's sedentary worker. In Paul's day, the people's daily routines included a high level of activity, so they derived less benefit from athletic exercise; but for today's sedentary worker, proper exercise is extremely important to mental and physical health. The undisciplined body will breed an undisciplined mind and soul. People who exercise regularly, however, find it easier to be disciplined in other aspects of their lives such as eating healthy diets, having regular devotions, holding their tempers, and many others. From the discipline of exercise, benefits spill over into many other areas of life, including the spiritual disciplines.

Exercise is also an essential part of any weight-loss program. Although thousands of diets claim that they will simply "burn" fat right off your tummy, buttocks, or thighs——research has shown that no diet, by itself, will lead to consistent weight loss over several weeks. If you have tried and stuck to several diets, you have probably found that for the first two to three weeks the pounds seemed to melt off; but soon you stopped losing weight. You probably blamed your dwindling weight loss on a single candy bar or piece of cake. Science has found that diets alone are almost always doomed to failure. The reason diets fail is that the body senses it is undergoing a time of starvation, so it begins to conserve energy by slowing down its metabolic rate. After three weeks on a diet you may still have been eating fewer calories; but your body had compensated by burning fewer calories.

An experiment will illustrate this point. Researchers put six obese patients on a diet of 3,500 calories per day for one week, and to no one's surprise the patients' weights stayed constant. Then the patients were restricted to a daily diet of only 450 calories. In three weeks, they lost an average of about ten pounds; but by the fourth week, they were no longer losing weight. When the researchers measured the patients' metabolic rates (by testing their oxygen consumption), they found that the dieters' metabolic rates had gone down along with their weights. Their bodies had adjusted to the state of starvation by conserving energy.

Do not despair, however, there is a way to force your body to burn extra energy even while you are on a diet. If you exercise, your body will increase its metabolic rate. Thus, you can continue to lose weight while you are on a diet.

What type of exercise is best? For almost all patients, I recom-

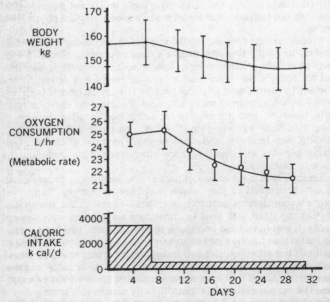

FIGURE 20: Changes in body weight and metabolic rate during a diet of 450 calories per day.[6]

mend brisk walking. Surprised? Did you think that I would say long-distance running or heavy weight training? Long-distance running, over a period of years, overstresses the knee and ankle joints, which may lead to arthritis. Almost all weight-training routines do not last long enough to produce beneficial effects on the heart. A brisk walk for at least one-half hour every day works the heart, burns up calories, and requires no more expense than a comfortable pair of shoes. Best of all, the time can be spent pondering Scripture, enjoying creation, confessing sin, praising God, and seeking His guidance.

In the last chapter, we saw that stress can lead to fatal heart attacks; but you may have asked, "How can stress on the brain lead to disease of the heart?" Researchers have found several factors that help explain these findings. In one experiment, doctors studied the blood of people undergoing very stressful medical procedures, such as having a catheter placed in the arteries of their hearts, kidneys, or livers. Before and during these procedures, the clotting cells (platelets) in their blood became much more responsive to a natural substance (ADP) that induces them to clot (see figure 21a). The stress of these procedures also led to elevated blood levels of free fatty acids, substances that are known to increase the rate of atheroma formation (see figure 21b). Thus, people who are suffering severe internal stress have blood that is more likely to clot, especially in a coronary artery that is already narrowed by an atheroma.

Now a further word about coping with psychic stress. Although medical science now knows some of the lethal chemicals that stress releases, medical science can offer little help to prevent stress from affecting people.

Statesmen boldly asserted in 1941 that they would eliminate man's mighty enemy—fear. Former President Franklin D. Roosevelt met with the great leaders of the world and incorporated in the Atlantic Charter the Four Freedoms. If it had come true, this charter would rank among the greatest documents of all ages, because it promised to all nations Four Freedoms, one of them—freedom from fear.

Four short years after this promise of millennial blessedness, the first atomic bomb was dropped, killing thousands and subjecting tens of thousands to excruciating suffering and lingering death. The realization that women, children, and the aged were now as vulnerable as the soldier on the front line gripped the world with a monstrous fear—the fear of total annihilation. H. G. Wells, reflecting the fear of that day, said "This world is at the end of its tether. The end of everything we call life is at hand."[7]

Speaking before the United Nations on September 26, 1961, the late President John F. Kennedy said, "Every man, woman and child

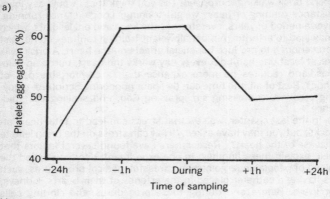

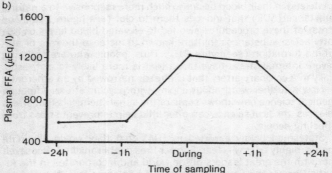

FIGURE 21: Platelet aggregation in response to ADP and plasma free fatty acid concentration: before, during, and after stressful medical procedures.[8]

lives under a nuclear sword of Damocles, hanging by the slenderest of threads, capable of being cut at any moment by accident, miscalculation, or madness.''

Today, we see a revival of this fear. Nightly news broadcasts tell us of the latest antinuke rally. Riots protesting the placement of nuclear missiles in Europe have shaken many of the political leaders of that continent. Catholic bishops have signed statements that condemn the arms race and call for disarmament.

One Book offers freedom from the stress of fear in this nuclear age. One Book has proven its value to millions subjected to all types

of fears. This Book of books abounds in assurances that God is in
control; thus, God's beloved need not fear:

> Surely he will save you from the fowler's snare
>   and under his wings you will find refuge. . . .
>   and from the deadly pestilence.
> He will cover you with his feathers,
>   and under his wings you will find refuge. . . .
> You will not fear the terror of night,
>   nor the arrow that flies by day,
> nor the pestilence that stalks in the darkness,
>   nor the plague that destroys at midday.
> A thousand may fall at your side,
>   ten thousand at your right hand,
>   but it will not come near you.
>
> Psalms 91:3-7 NIV

Scoffers will retort, "Don't you know that nuclear warheads are so
powerful that one of them dropped on New York City would kill over
4 million people?" Perhaps the Lord inspired the writer to record
Psalm 46 for us in this nuclear age:

> God is our refuge and strength,
>   an ever present help in trouble.
> Therefore we will not fear,
>   though the earth give way
>   and the mountains fall into the heart of the sea,
> though its waters roar and foam
>   and the mountains quake with their surging.
>
> Come and see the works of the Lord. . . .
> He makes wars cease to the ends of the earth;
>   he breaks the bow and shatters the spear,
>   he burns the shields with fire.
> "Be still, and know that I am God;
>   I will be exalted among the nations,
>   I will be exalted in the earth."
> The Lord Almighty is with us;
>   the God of Jacob is our fortress.
>
> Psalms 46:1-3, 9-11 NIV

Today the world outlook is darker than at any previous time in
history. Many declare that a nuclear holocaust is both imminent and
inevitable. They fear that man, the consummation of "milennia of
evolution," will disappear in a global nuclear inferno as a victim of
the very thing that "created" him—"Chance." Yet the Christian

need not fear that, because of some unfortunate slipup, the ultimate victory will go to a nuclear superpower. In his Revelation, John saw who will emerge victorious from the final conflict:

> I saw heaven standing open and there before me was a white horse, whose rider is called Faithful and True. . . . The armies of heaven were following him. . . . On his robe and on his thigh he has this name written:
> KING OF KINGS AND LORD OF LORDS. . . .
> Then I saw the beast and the kings of the earth and their armies gathered together to make war against the rider on the horse and his army. But the beast was captured, and with him the false prophet. . . . The two of them were thrown alive into the fiery lake of burning sulfur. The rest of them were killed with the sword that came out of the mouth of the rider on the horse, and all the birds gorged themselves on their flesh.
>
> Revelation 19:11,14,16,19–21 NIV

To the Christian the overwhelming sense of doom in the world is only an indication of the imminent and glorious return of Jesus Christ. The believer need not fear; for the nuclear weapons of man will be as useless as cream pies when they are launched against the Potentate of Time. As times grow worse, the Christian can look up; for his deliverance is close at hand.

Chapter Seventeen

David and the Giant— Worry

"Doctor, I came to you because I'm worn out. Before this thing hit me, I could work all day and not get tired. When I drove the tractor yesterday, I got so weak that I had to stop before I got halfway across the field. I had to get off the tractor and lie down by the fence before I got enough strength to go on. That's not like me. For the past month, I've been completely bushed. I've been losing weight, too."

I stared in amazement at Joe, a husky twenty-year-old farmer. He was the type who never got sick, yet here he stood——wholly incapacitated for work. His tiredness could have been signaling a serious disorder, so my first thoughts were of anemia, leukemia, or perhaps internal bleeding. The possibility of cancer and tuberculosis came to my mind. Physical examination and laboratory tests, however, found no organic trouble.

I questioned Joe more carefully, and I discovered that his attractive fiancée had recently started dating another guy. Also, a man who had promised to give Joe a good bargain on a used car had now raised the price $200. The fear of losing both girl and car had already caused Joe to lose his appetite, his sleep, and his strength.

Yes, this young man's fatigue was entirely due to worry and anxiety. Many scientific studies have shown that long and continued stress completely exhausts a person. I explained the situation to Joe

153

and gave him a few antianxiety tablets. Within a week, his normal strength came back; and his appearance and personality improved so much that he won and married the girl of his choice. Not work but worry had made him weary.

Perhaps you have had a similar experience. Some days you work hard from early morning until late at night without experiencing fatigue. Then, another day, you are worn out by the middle of the day. Next time you have such unusual weariness, pause and think; often you will be able to remember some emotional upset. It may not be anything more than the boss looking over your sales record and asking, "Is that the best you can do?" Or you may have worn a new dress, one you made yourself, and not a single person in the office made a comment about it.

Patients often tell me that they are just as tired when they wake up as when they went to bed. Sleep refreshes the healthy exhaustion of hard work but not the harmful weariness of constant worry. Far too many people take their anxieties to bed with them.

Anxiety can manifest itself in other ways. Psychiatrist A. Scott Dowling tells of such a patient: "A 17-year-old boy, while recounting a vivid recollection of being beaten and choked by his father, threw his head back and clutched his hands over his throat but did not touch his skin. As he sobbed and spoke in an agonized way of these experiences, erythema [redness] and extensive linear wheals appeared over his neck."[1]

One day a mother brought her son to my office. His entire body was plastered with red, itchy, and painful wheals. His mother was puzzled, "Doctor, what causes my Tony to break out like this? He never had hives until the past few months. His diet hasn't changed."

She hesitated. When I urged her to continue, she laughed and said, "You may think I am foolish, but Tony gets hives only when he spends the whole day with his aunt. She moved into our home recently, and she's fanatical about keeping the house spick-and-span. It is true Tony is a careless youngster, but his aunt scolds and nags him constantly. Fear of her couldn't possibly——?"

"Oh, yes," I replied. "Many times hives are triggered by an emotional upset." I advised her to keep Tony away from his aunt as much as possible. They bought a mobile home for his aunt so that she could live nearby but would not bother Tony. "Cured," Tony never had another attack of hives.

Asthma can also be triggered by stress. Gasping for air during an asthmatic attack induces fear and tension, which further aggravate the condition a great deal by establishing a vicious circle of anxiety, then wheezing, then more anxiety, then more wheezing, and so on.

One study found that one-half of asthmatics will develop a full-blown asthmatic attack if they are just *told* that they are being exposed to a pollen or other aggravating substance.[2] If these patients are pretreated with a drug that blocks a chemical (acetylcholine) that causes contraction of the airways, these patients no longer suffer attacks when they are told that they are in the presence of an aggravating substance.[3] Again, we see the importance of chemicals (in this case, acetylcholine) released by anxiety in causing disease (in this case, asthma).

Many observers feel that children with asthma tend to see their parents as overbearing or rejecting. In one study researchers sent parents of asthmatic children on paid vacations and left trained observers to take care of the children. Without any other treatment, about half of the children improved.[4]

A psychiatrist once told me of a patient who developed asthma every time he heard a church bell ring. His trouble began several years before, while he was waiting for his bride to arrive at the church. The church bells were chiming to announce this glorious occasion, when a messenger arrived with the news that his fiancée had changed her mind. The emotional shock triggered a severe asthma attack in the man. In the years that followed, every time he heard a church bell, he was seized with an attack of asthma.

The Psalmist David had more reasons than most of us to have justifiable fears. Consider his encounters with a savage lion, a ferocious bear, the gigantic Goliath, the murderous King Saul, and his treacherous son Absalom. David saved himself from psychosomatic disease because he always put his trust in the Lord:

> The Lord is my light and my salvation—
>   whom shall I fear?
> The Lord is the stronghold of my life—
>   of whom shall I be afraid?
> Though an army besiege me,
>   my heart will not fear;
> though war break out against me,
> even then will I be confident.
>   Psalms 27:1,3 NIV

High blood pressure can be caused not only by hostility, as previously shown, but also by worry. This was clearly demonstrated during the siege of Leningrad in World War II. While the city was under siege, doctors observed a massive outbreak of high blood pressure within the city.[5]

In one experiment, monkeys had to press a bar every twenty sec-

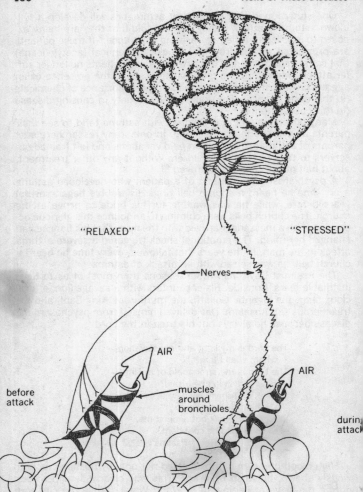

"RELAXED"

"STRESSED"

← Nerves →

AIR

AIR

before attack

muscles around bronchioles

during attack

air sacs

FIGURE 22: Emotional upset always irritates and sometimes causes asthma attacks.

onds for twelve hours a day in order to avoid electrical shocks. After several months these monkeys developed high blood pressure. But even more astounding were the skyrocketing blood pressures of these monkeys if the bar was removed from their cage. The monkeys constantly worried about not being able to avoid the shocks even though no shocks were delivered.[6] These researchers showed that the arteries to the skin, kidneys, intestines, and muscles of these monkeys were contracted; and this caused the tremendous increases in blood pressure.[7] As squeezing on the end of a garden hose causes a buildup in pressure within that hose, so these blood-pressure increases were due to adrenaline causing the arteries to contract.

If researchers place a mouse cage in a room with a caged cat, these mice develop high blood pressure in six to twelve months. Even though the cat never even chases the mice, the constant worrying of the mice subjects them to the serious disease of high blood pressure.[8]

Dr. Frank Backus has said, "Most patients with hypertension [high blood pressure] feel that they are being threatened and have to be ready for anything."[9] This constant activation of the fight or flight response with its accompanied release of adrenaline causes contraction of the arteries, which causes increased blood pressure. This mechanism is thought to be responsible for many, but definitely not all, cases of high blood pressure.

All of us have had and will continue to have encounters with the giant worry, so let us recall a bit of history. Remember when King Saul and his mighty army were cowering at the mere words of the giant Goliath? The stripling David was stirred by Israel's lack of faith in God. Refusing the accepted methods of fighting giants, David went out armed with a mighty faith in God, a leather sling in his hand, and five smooth stones in his pocket. Was he afraid?

> When I am afraid,
> I will trust in you.
> In God, whose word I praise,
> in God I trust; I will not be afraid.
> What can mortal man do to me?
> Psalms 56:3,4 NIV

David's faith was bound to conquer, and conquer it did. In our everyday encounters with big and little worries, the practice of our faith decides whether we cower or conquer. David was able to conquer not only Goliath; but on many occasions, God also gave him the strength to conquer the giant worry. Perhaps that is one reason why his psalms are so helpful in dealing with worry.

No prescription has ever helped more people deal with worry than the Twenty-third Psalm. It can be taken with meals, before retiring, and as often as needed. It will give a man energy to be more than a conqueror over the giant worry and his lethal ally, disease:

> The Lord is my shepherd; I shall not want.
>> He maketh me to lie down in green pastures:
> he leadeth me beside the still waters.
>> He restoreth my soul:
> He leadeth me in the paths of righteousness
>> for his name's sake.
> Yea, though I walk
>> through the valley of the shadow of death,
> I will fear no evil:
>> for thou art with me;
> thy rod and thy staff
>> they comfort me.
> Thou preparest a table before me
>> in the presence of mine enemies:
> thou anointest my head with oil;
>> my cup runneth over.
> Surely goodness and mercy shall follow me
>> all the days of my life:
> and I will dwell in the house of the Lord
>> for ever.

(KJV)

Chapter Eighteen

Man's Greatest Fear

 Nearly everybody has been in a J. C. Penney store, one of the world's largest chains of department stores. But few people know about one of the most important events in the life of J. C. Penney, the founder.

Surviving the economic crash of 1929, J. C. Penney's business was solid, but he had made a few unwise personal commitments. These commitments worried him so much that he couldn't sleep at night. The stress from this chronic fatigue depressed his immune system, and he suffered a relapse of the chicken-pox virus that had been silently hiding in his nerves ever since he had the rash as a child. The recurrence of this virus is called shingles—a disease that causes great annoyance and severe pain. He was hospitalized and given sedatives, but he got no relief and tossed all night. A combination of circumstances had broken him so completely, physically and mentally, that he was overwhelmed with a fear of death. He wrote farewell letters to his wife and son, for he did not expect to live until morning.

The next morning the business tycoon awoke to singing in the hospital chapel. He pulled himself together and entered as the group was singing "God Will Take Care of You." Following a Scripture reading and a prayer, "Suddenly," as Mr. Penney has written,

159

"something happened. I can't explain it. I can only call it a miracle. I felt as if I had been instantly lifted out of the darkness of a dungeon into warm, brilliant sunlight. I felt as if I had been transported from hell to paradise. I felt the power of God as I had never felt it before. I realized then that I alone was responsible for all my troubles. I knew that God with His love was there to help me. From that day to this, my life has been free from worry. I am seventy-one years old, and the most dramatic and glorious minutes of my life were those I spent in that chapel that morning: 'God Will Take Care of You' "[1]

Thus, a man who had been through "the valley of the shadow of death" found freedom from fear in a loving, heavenly Father—his Father, a Father ready and willing to take care of him in life's dilemmas.

William Ewart Gladstone told of his secret for maintaining his unusual serenity despite many situational stresses: "At the foot of my bed, where I can see it on retiring and on arising in the morning, are the words, 'Thou wilt keep him in perfect peace, whose mind is stayed on thee: because he trusteth in thee' " (Isaiah 26:3 KJV).

Dr. William Sadler in his textbook of psychiatry wrote:

> Prayer is a powerful and effectual worry-remover. Men and women who have learned to pray with childlike sincerity, literally talking to, and communing with the Heavenly Father, are in possession of the great secret whereby they can cast their care upon God, knowing that He careth for us. A clear conscience is a great step toward barricading the mind against neuroticism.
>
> Many are victims of fear and worry because they fail properly to maintain their spiritual nutrition. . . . The majority of people liberally feed their bodies, and many make generous provision for their mental nourishment; but the vast majority leave the soul to starve, paying very little attention to their spiritual nutrition; and as a result the spiritual nature is so weakened that it is unable to surmount its difficulties and maintain an atmosphere above conflict and despondency.[2]

He further advised physicians to encourage their patients to engage "in daily, systematic Bible reading." In fact, in his textbook, Dr. Sadler wrote forty-three different verses as examples of the therapeutic value of Bible reading. I only list seven here. Each of them, if assimilated into the mind and put into action, can accomplish more than any sedative or tranquilizer.

If we confess our sins, he is faithful and just to forgive us our sins, and to cleanse us from all unrighteousness.

1 John 1:9 KJV

Come unto me, all ye that labour and are heavy laden, and I will give you rest. Take my yoke upon you, and learn of me; for I am meek and lowly in heart: and ye shall find rest unto your souls.

Matthew 11:28,29 KJV

Create in me a clean heart, O God; and renew a right spirit within me.

Psalms 51:10 KJV

Peace I leave with you, my peace I give unto you: not as the world giveth, give I unto you. Let not your heart be troubled, neither let it be afraid.

John 14:27 KJV

But my God shall supply all your need according to his riches in glory by Christ Jesus.

Philippians 4:19 KJV

I can do all things through Christ which strengtheneth me.

Philippians 4:13 KJV

For he shall give his angels charge over thee, to keep thee in all thy ways. They shall bear thee up in their hands, lest thou dash thy foot against a stone.

Psalms 91:11,12 KJV

These verses become alive and real only after we have experienced their therapeutic value. I remember the night, many years ago, when I asked God to forgive my sins. Faced with an overwhelming sense of guilt, I felt the horrible weight of all my sins; and fear gripped my soul. After confessing and forsaking my sin, the guilt and fears vanished; and a miraculous, heaven-sent joy filled my heart. Instead of interminable, expensive trips to a psychiatrist's couch to get rid of a disease-producing guilt complex, I made one trip to God's altar and got rid of guilt itself.

The Bible says that God removes the guilt "as far as the east is from the west" (see Psalms 103:12 KJV). Relief from guilt freed my soul from the clutches of fear. The Lord replaced my fear and guilt with peace and gratitude. I experienced what John wrote: "There is no fear in love; but perfect love casteth out fear . . ." (1 John 4:18 KJV). As love increases, fear decreases.

Love for Christ and His Word helped Jim Vaus when he needed relief from fear. Before his conversion, Jim had been the wiretapper for the infamous underworld gang of Mickey Cohen in Los Angeles. The morning after his conversion at a Billy Graham crusade, the newspapers blazoned the story about Jim Vaus, the gangster for Christ.

When Jim Vaus read the morning papers, he began to do some serious thinking. What would the gangsters decide to do with him? After all, Jim knew many secrets that might send most of the gang to the penitentiary, if not to the gas chamber. From the gang's viewpoint, Jim's conversion meant he had turned traitor to them; he knew that the gang would arrange for a speedy execution.

After laying the paper aside, he didn't have long to wait. As he looked out the window, a big limousine stopped in front of his house. Jim recognized the men who emerged as some of the most ruthless gangsters in the underworld. Looking suspiciously up and down the street, they approached his front door.

If ever a man had reason to run in fear for his life, he did. If he had been in such danger twenty-four hours earlier, he certainly would have fled——and probably would still be running. But he didn't run; for when he opened his Bible at random that morning, his loving Father had strengthened him with a specific verse: "When a man's ways please the Lord, he maketh even his enemies to be at peace with him" (Proverbs 16:7 KJV).

Jim opened the door to the gunmen. They told him that a wire-tapping job in St. Louis had been assigned to him. Jim told them he couldn't go because the Lord had changed his heart. When he described his conversion, his visitors looked bewildered and left. Jim knew that the Lord had fulfilled the promise He had given him.

The "dread of death" has always been man's greatest fear. Millions of men and women, however, have gone through "the valley of the shadow of death" without apprehension. John Bunyan expressed the proper attitude for a Christian: "Let dissolution come when it will, it can do the Christian no harm, for it be but a passage out of a prison into a palace; out of a sea of troubles into a haven of rest; out of a crowd of enemies, to an innumerable company of true, loving, and faithful friends; out of shame, reproach, and contempt into exceeding great and eternal glory."

The Apostle Paul, a man who faced man's greatest fear many times, exultingly exclaimed, "When the perishable has been clothed with the imperishable, and the mortal with immortality, then the saying that is written will come true: 'Death has been swallowed up in victory.' "

> "Where, O death, is your victory?
> Where, O death, is your sting?"
> 1 Corinthians 15:54,55 NIV

Truly, in every age the Spirit and Word of God have provided abundant deliverance for Christians from fear and the diseases that it causes. Even the master of all fears, death, should hold no terror for the believer who looks patiently and expectantly for the day when, "The trumpet shall sound, and the dead shall be raised incorruptible, and we shall be changed" (1 Corinthians 15:52 KJV).

Only the Christian is able to heed the advice of William Cullen Bryant:

> So live, that when thy summons comes to join
> The innumerable caravan, which moves
> To that mysterious realm, where each shall take
> His chamber in the silent halls of death,
> Thou go not, like the quarry-slave at night,
> Scourged to his dungeon, but, sustained and soothed
> By an unfaltering trust, approach thy grave,
> Like one who wraps the drapery of his couch
> About him, and lies down to pleasant dreams.[3]

Chapter Nineteen

"See Farther Through a Tear Than Through a Telescope"

 Late one afternoon, I walked up the sidewalk to the house of a healthy young married woman. In the western skies the sun was painting a mural of reds and oranges, but I did not see any beauty in it. I rang the doorbell and waited. It seemed like hours, and I wished that it would take even longer, until Mary—a pretty twenty-five-year-old woman—cheerfully answered the door. "Hi, Doctor Mac. Come in and have some iced tea. Jack should be home any . . ." Just then she noticed the grave look on my face. "Doc, what's wrong?"

"It's Jack," I said. "He was in an accident on Route 19. It happened instantaneously. There wasn't anything that we could do."

Any of us can sympathize with her for the grief that she experienced during the evening and long hours of the night when she couldn't sleep. The one who meant everything to her had been cruelly snatched away. For days, she was so completely and irreconcilably overwhelmed with grief that she refused to listen to her worried doctor and sympathetic friends.

If a hospital lab had analyzed her blood, they would have found a great increase in hormones from her pituitary and adrenal glands. The toxicity of these compounds was sadly demonstrated as her wrist joints soon stiffened, swelled, and became very painful. This was the onset of an arthritis that eventually invalided the young woman.

Thus, we see that hate and fear are not the only emotions capable of producing serious and sometimes fatal disease. Excessive grief can also damage the body. Grief seems to trigger onsets of ulcerative colitis, rheumatoid arthritis, coronary artery disease, and many other diseases.

To prevent the outbreak of diseases resulting from inconsolable grief, the Bible provides the greatest possible barricade. The eleventh chapter of John not only gives clear teaching on this matter but also presents public and dramatic proof of the veracity of this teaching. In the village of Bethany lived a family, Lazarus and his sisters Mary and Martha, who knew and loved Jesus. When Lazarus became sick, they sent word to Jesus for help. But Jesus intentionally delayed His response because He wanted to teach the world about the transitory character of the state we call death. When Jesus started His trip to Bethany, He told His disciples that He was going to raise Lazarus out of his sleep.

The disciples thought it was rather ridiculous to make a long and hazardous journey just to wake a sick man out of sleep, so Jesus talked to them in the only language that they could understand: "Lazarus is dead" (John 11:14 NIV).

Arriving in Bethany, Jesus revealed to Martha, who was mourning for her dead brother, another important aspect of the state that we erroneously call death: "I am the resurrection and the life. He who believes in me will live, even though he dies; and whoever lives and believes in me will never die. Do you believe this?" (John 11:25,26 NIV).

How could anybody believe that people could live through an experience like death—that they were only asleep? Jesus knew that even His disciples and many others at Bethany would find it difficult to believe such assertions without proof. A million empty human words, no matter how well said, would have convinced very few; but the result of three words from the Master convinced many who saw it: "Lazarus, come forth." Out came Lazarus, living proof that death is temporary. For the Christian there is no horrible existence associated with the word *death*. Death is only a sleep that requires the call of the Christ to awaken us. Influenced by this radical view of death, Christians began to call their graveyards, "sleeping chambers." In fact, the Christian viewpoint even affected the English language, for the English word "cemetery" comes from the Greek *koimeterion*, which means "sleeping chamber."

When Jesus told those who were mourning over the dead body of Jairus's daughter, ". . . She is not dead, but asleep" (Luke 8:52 NIV), they ridiculed Him. Again He wanted to prove false the utterly hopeless view we erroneously hold concerning the state we call death. So He merely took the cold and motionless girl by the hand and "awakened" her.

Paul also wrote to Christians who had suffered the temporary loss of loved ones: "Brothers, we do not want you to be ignorant about those who fall asleep, or to grieve like the rest of men, who have no hope" (1 Thessalonians 4:13 NIV). Neither should we grieve today over our children and loved ones who are asleep in their bedrooms. Of course, we can be excused if we shed some tears over the separation; but Christians must believe what Jesus proved about the promise of their awakening. We need not grieve with such bitter and tumultuous emotion that we bring down upon ourselves attacks of arthritis and other diseases. It is both a wonderful privilege and an inescapable duty for believers to refrain from despairing when loved ones die; for we know that our loved ones, though absent from our immediate presence, are sleeping.

When Sheldon Vanauken was immersed in grief for his recently departed wife, C. S. Lewis gently chided his dear friend in a letter, "Death—corruption—resurrection is the true rhythm: not the pathetic, horrible practice of mummification. Sad you must be at present. You can't develop a false sense of a duty to cling to sadness if—and when, for nature will not preserve any psychological state forever—sadness begins to vanish."[1]

Grief is a natural and important part of life. In fact, psychologists speak of an "insufficient time of bereavement." It is truly important that we mourn the loss of a loved one. However, we must never forget that we are grieving for our own loss—a loss that has been our loved one's gain.

Equally important, we must remember God's promise: ". . . The dead in Christ will rise first. Then we who are alive and remain shall be caught up together with them in the clouds to meet the Lord in the air. And thus we shall always be with the Lord. Therefore comfort one another with these words" (1 Thessalonians 4:16–18 NKJB-NT). C. S. Lewis shouted his last earthly farewell to his dear friend Sheldon Vanauken across a busy street, "Christians NEVER say goodbye!"[2]

Someone has expressed this temporary separation in another way: "I love to think of my little children whom God has called to Himself as away at school—at the best school in the universe, under the best teachers, learning the best things, in the best possible way."

Some may wonder why God allows His children to experience sorrow at all. However, we must remember that death was not a part of God's original plan for man but a result of Adam's disobedience.

Paul reminds us, ". . . death came through a man . . ." (1 Corinthians 15:21 NIV). Man, not God, must bear the responsibility for the curse of death. Throughout this book we have repeatedly seen that disease and death are products of our own sin; we can't blame God for them. Instead, we ought to praise God for our deliverance from the ultimate disease—death: "For just as in Adam all die, so in Christ all will be made alive" (1 Corinthians 15:22 NIV). God is not the author of death, but the Giver of eternal life.

Not only in the future, but also in this present life, the divine Alchemist can miraculously change a grieving heart of lead into a joyful spirit of gold: a spirit that can sing praises through tears. What an exciting truth! The sorrows that cause irreconcilable grief and devastating diseases in some people can in others develop firm character and substantial maturity. For the object being polished, the polishing is not a pleasant process; but every stone that becomes a gem must be polished first. We admire the finished product, but we shrink from the process.

In December 1961, a letter brought sorrow to our home. Our daughter and her husband were missionaries in Zimbabwe. Then came a letter from her, written in a hospital where she had been a patient for several weeks. An examination of her spinal fluid had revealed an abundance of a deadly fungus, Candida. The well-trained English physicians had started her on a medication—but only as a gesture, for they were well aware that no effective treatment was yet known for this infection.

What sadness and anxiety gripped my wife and me! Never before could we fully appreciate the loss of those whose children had died.

Our grief might well have overwhelmed us if it had not been for the comfort and solace of the Holy Spirit and the inspired Scriptures. We wondered how people who do not know Christ are able to bear such great sorrow. Infinitely more effective than any tranquilizer, the wonder drug of Scripture relieved our emotional tension: "For this slight momentary trouble is producing for us an everlasting weight of glory that exceeds all measures, because we do not fasten our eyes on the visible but on the unseen; for the visible things are transitory, but the unseen things are everlasting" (2 Corinthians 4:17,18 MLB).

We saw that our crushing load of sorrow need not result in overwhelming grief. Instead, it could give us "an everlasting weight of glory that exceeds all calculations. . . ." Our attitude would determine whether our grief would lead to deep and unending depression or glorious and everlasting reward. It was our privilege to look through our tears and see farther than through any telescope—beyond the troubles and confinement of this fleeting universe to the comfort and glory of the eternal heaven.

Observe the condition: "granted we do not fasten our eyes on the visible but on the unseen." An unreasonable condition? After all, if we have the proper sense of proportion between transitory happiness and eternal glory, how can we mourn without accepting the solace that Scripture provides? Is it not an expression of selfishness to mourn our own loss so unduly and persistently that we harm our own health? And is it not a confession of doubt to mourn so? If our temporary loss of their presence has opened the gates of eternal glory for our loved one, how can true love mourn without finding comfort in their gain? And what is more, these momentary troubles are earning for us an "eternal glory" that will make our troubles pale in comparison.

Sorrow can cause diseases in us if we continue to grieve over the past. The Bible erases irreconcilable grief and prevents disease by telling us to look to the future.

In the weeks that followed the receipt of our daughter's first letter, the Word and Holy Spirit of God made life bearable for us. We had peace of mind because we committed everything to Him.

My daughter, her husband, and their two babies (David and his sister) were flown home. I can still see her sitting in a wheelchair in the corridor of the airport—her ashen face drained of all energy. She could hardly muster the effort to speak.

That night David was so worried for his mother that he would not go to sleep. I tried to comfort him, but I could not. Then he revealed his future bent for medicine by asking, "Will they give her a Band-Aid?" I assured him that they would. Knowing that his mother was in competent hands, he soon fell asleep—a lesson for all of us who sing, "He's Got the Whole World in His Hands."

Linda was studied thoroughly at a major medical center, but no fungus or bacteria was found in repeated spinal-fluid examinations. However, pus cells in her spinal fluid belied the negative tests and signaled the presence of some organism, festering within the tissue coverings of her brain. Although Linda continued to have a low-grade fever, a severe headache, a stiff neck, and persistent vomiting—the specialists were hesitant to start treatment with antibiotics. After two months, however, her physician husband and I consulted the experts; and we decided to start treating with penicillin. Large doses of penicillin killed whatever bug was causing the meningitis; and her symptoms disappeared. After a month on the high dosage, a spinal tap showed that the spinal fluid had returned to normal.

The Lord allowed Linda to recover from that infection, give birth to two more daughters, and see all four of her children graduate from high school. But her bout with meningitis was not her last walk through the valley of the shadow of premature death. In the spring of 1981, we found out that she had a rare cancer. Up to that time, this cancer had been almost universally fatal; but a new drug held some promise. Her doctors, however, were not very hopeful. She underwent radical surgery and one full year of grueling chemotherapy. Her hair fell out, and she often felt nauseated. Again, we were forced to look to the Scriptures and their promises; and once again they allowed us to bear our anxiety with a spirit of reconciled and subdued joy.

Since her surgery, almost three years have passed. Will Linda's cancer return? Has her medical treatment just postponed inevitable death from this cancer? We do not know. We do not know what the future holds, but we do know who holds the future. Faith in a loving omnipotent God has allowed us to say, with Paul, "Entertain no worry, but under all circumstances let your petitions be made known before God by prayer and pleading along with thanksgiving. So will the peace of God, that surpasses all understanding, keep guard over your hearts and your thoughts in Christ Jesus" (Philippians 4:6,7 MLB).

Linda, her husband, and all of us thank the Lord, not for causing pain and sorrow—for we, as sinful humans, have brought that upon ourselves—but for using her experiences in the valley of the shadow of death. Through these experiences He has matured us and given "us an everlasting weight of glory that exceeds all calculations." As we continue to gaze through our tears beyond this visible yet transitory life, endearing to us though it may be, faith in God allows us to see farther through a tear than through a telescope. Through faith we can fix our eyes on the invisible yet eternal life promised to all who believe in Jesus the Messiah.

Chapter Twenty

Mud or Stars?

*Two men look out through the same bars:
One sees the mud, and one the stars.*[1]

 This observation was recorded long before any of us kicked at the slats in our cribs. Scientists, however, did not demonstrate the medical significance of these attitudes until this century. The two men who looked through the same prison bars reacted completely differently to the same stresses of imprisonment: one was frustrated by the bars, whereas the other was inspired by the stars. The frustrated man suffered the stress of earthly frustration; the other enjoyed the beauty of God's creation.

Dr. Theodore R. Miller, a well-known cancer surgeon, recognizes the influence of a cancer patient's outlook on survival. He states, "Patients who are apprehensive about their disease almost always do badly and die rapidly, even though the cancer is treated at an early stage. . . . I no longer operate on a patient who expresses the fear that he would not survive the operation."[2] In one study of patients undergoing open-heart surgery, doctors found that 75 percent of the depressed patients died; but only 15 percent of all other patients died.[3] Depressed patients had given up, and had resigned themselves to untimely death—a self-fulfilled "death wish." Although they underwent the same stresses of open-heart surgery, many of the patients in this study died because of their negative outlooks—negative outlooks that left them powerless to cope with the stress of surgery.

Our outlooks on life have tremendous significance long before doctors start to treat for disease. In 1957, scientists administered psychological tests to 2,020 middle-aged employees of Western Electric. During the ensuing seventeen years, men who were rated as "psychologically depressed" in 1957 had a cancer death rate that was twice that of the other men in the study. The effect of depression on the cancer death rate remained even if the figures were adjusted for age, cigarette smoking, alcohol use, family history of cancer, and occupational status. Thus, if we do not smoke or drink, our outlook on life may be the most important factor in determining whether we will die from cancer![4]

Stress factors affect us all, but we can react in many different ways. Our internal reactions to stress determine how the stress will affect us. Physicians now recognize the great importance of this internal stress in the causation and aggravation of many diseases.

Two prisoners were subjected to the same stress factors, but only one developed inner stress and exposed himself to disease. Examination of his blood would have revealed harmful levels of certain hormones that were called forth as a result of his emotions of frustration, resentment, anger, hate, anxiety and fear—the same brood of carnal emotions referred to in previous chapters.

One needs to distinguish between inner stress, which one experiences within the body, and external stress factors. All of us are subjected to many, many stress factors in our daily lives; but that does not mean we have to develop inner stress with its resultant toxic hormone levels and diseases. One of the men subjected to the external stress factors of prison bars was actually inspired by the stars—stars he may never have noticed before.

There are great differences in the ways people react to such stress factors as smashing a new car into a telephone pole, giving a controversial speech to an antagonistic audience, returning a defective refrigerator to a department store, disciplining an unruly child for insubordinate behavior, or chasing a pesky dog out of a flower bed. Physicians are kept busy treating people who react poorly to stressful situations. Some patients develop sieges of abdominal distress that last three or four weeks and require a great deal of medication. Others suffer the agonies of severe migraine headaches with vomiting, incapacitating them for a day or two. Many succumb to heart attacks.

On the other hand, some people who are subjected to the identical stress factors adapt well and experience few ill effects. We often have little control over what stress factors daily bombard us.

Thus, if we are to save our bodies and minds from the ravages of stress-induced diseases, we must learn to cope properly with these stress factors.

The importance of proper coping with stress has been sadly demonstrated by prisoners of war in every war of this century. Among every group of POWs there were those who could see nothing but mud. For example, of the 31,000 servicemen imprisoned during the Korean War over 8,000 died. Dr. Harold Wolff has described a certain type of reaction to imprisonment that was responsible for many of these deaths. He states that even though this prisoner was given enough food to eat, "the prisoner became apathetic, listless, neither ate nor drank, helped himself in no way, stared into space and finally died." Dr. Wolff states that many of these deaths were caused by "despair and deprivation of human support and affection." Dr. Wolff, who was editor-in-chief of *Archives of Neurology and Psychiatry,* concluded that "Hope, like faith and a purpose in life, is medicinal. This is not merely a statement of belief, but a conclusion proved by meticulously controlled scientific experiment."[5]

Another prisoner could see stars. Such a man was my esteemed Japanese friend Dr. David Tsutada. When Japan entered World War II, the Japanese government put him in prison because of his belief that Christ would return and rule the earth. He was given so little food that his weight dropped to seventy pounds. His captors confined him to a filthy, cold, damp hole in the ground. As he sat on the floor, he wondered if this was the way the Lord was going to take him home to heaven. If it was, he was resigned to it. He wasn't frustrated by the bars or the mud or the Lord's apparent lack of care for him. If Dr. Tsutada had not coped with the situation by accepting and using it, I am convinced that the stress of anger and self-pity, added to the severe stress of starvation, would have killed him.

However, while he was in prison, the Lord began to reveal to him plans for a Bible school. Dr. Tsutada worked out many details for the school while he sat in the darkness and stench of his cell. When the war was over, he was released, and he immediately put his plans into operation. Under God's direction, he founded one of the finest Bible-training schools in Japan because he didn't fret about evildoers but trusted and delighted in God's Word (see Psalm 37).

Few people were ever behind as many bars as Helen Keller—blind, deaf, and dumb—yet she became immortal in the annals of mankind because she utilized her adversities as stepping-stones in climbing out of her dark, silent dungeon to encourage the world with her spirit and love.

We should not unduly fear life's difficulties or go to great lengths to avoid them. Strong contrary winds need not blow us to destruction. In fact, the intelligent sailor can adjust his sails properly so that even adverse winds power him to his goal. Contrary people can help us if we make the necessary adjustments in our mental rigging. On the water they call it tacking, but on land they call it tact.

By concentrating on things beyond this world, John Bunyan forgot about the prison bars. God blessed not only John Bunyan but millions of others with the classic book *Pilgrim's Progress*. In one of his other books Bunyan gave excellent advice for preparing for stresses even before they strike. It is as true today as it was three hundred years ago:

> While we are at ease [and] have our comforts about us, let us look for troubles; afflictions from God, as well as for God, are part of our cross which we must take up daily. Sickness, death of friends, loss of estate, etc., we must look for them that we may not be surprised.
>
> So it must be our care to provide for afflictions; for to prevent them altogether we cannot; but prepare for them we may, and must. . . . To treasure up God's promises, and store our souls with graces, and spiritual comforts, and firm resolutions in God's strength, to bear up and to hold on: we need be well "shod with the preparation of the gospel of peace," Ephesians 6:15.
>
> Most Christians are not mortified and crucified to the world, not acquainted with God and the promises as they ought to be, nor so resolved to follow God fully, as they ought, and therefore are so dejected and discontented when affliction comes.[6]

Here is solid truth. Since our attitudes of mind are more important than the daily insults of life, we should condition our minds before life's major catastrophes hit us. Armies recognize this basic truth and put their troops through rigorous training. If Christians would practice biblical disciplines——such as fasting, meditation, solitude, and prayer——we would not have so many "chocolate soldiers" who melt and crumble when they are forced to endure hot and fierce experiences such as the unexpected death of a loved one, loss of a worldly fortune, or persecution of a hostile government.

Jacob looked at mud and grabbed for the things of mud even from the moment of his birth. At his birth, he was grabbing the heel of his twin brother. As soon as he was able to trade, he created a black market in pottage and traded a little of it for his brother's birthright. He even became a rich man by outtricking that former master of chicanery——his father-in-law, Laban.

How would you expect a character like Jacob to react to stress? When he was told that his favorite son, Joseph, had been killed, there was nothing wrong in the natural sorrow he felt. But he was not able to properly cope with the stress, and he continued to weep long after he should have stopped. To those who sought to comfort him, he said "I want to go down to the grave mourning for my son" (Genesis 37:35 MLB). He preferred basking in self-pity to accepting the reality of his son's death. The man who never learns to adjust properly to stress never becomes mature.

Jacob insisted on looking at mud instead of believing that even misfortunes can be an important part of God's blueprints, as was certainly the case with him. His tears were entirely wasted; for God had actually preserved Joseph. It would appear that Jacob thought God had also died, for all he could do was groan, ". . . Everything is against me" (Genesis 42:36 NIV).

His body evidently suffered the results of his maladjustment, for near the close of his life, he grunted, "Few and strenuous my life's days and years have been and not equal to the pilgrim years of my father's . . ." (Genesis 47:9 MLB).

Now Paul had far more assaults to withstand than Jacob, but he saw the stars: "Five times I received from the Jews forty lashes minus one; three times I was beaten with rods; once I was stoned, three times I was shipwrecked, for a night and a day I have been adrift at sea. In my many travels I have been in dangers of rivers and robbers, of Jews and Gentiles, of city, desert, and sea; in dangers among false brothers; in wearying work and hardship through many a sleepless night; in hunger, thirst, and often without food; in cold and lack of clothing" (2 Corinthians 11:24–27 MLB). In these frightful situations did Paul ever moan, "All these things are against me"? On the contrary, he exclaimed, "None of these things move me" (Acts 20:24 KJV). Refusing to wallow in self-pity, he protected his body from disease-producing hormones. What was the secret of Paul's successful adaptation to these many stressful agents? What enabled him to adapt to repeated scourgings, stonings, and starvations?

Let us analyze the method for coping with stresses that Paul used and taught. After listing stressful agents that assail mankind, he gives the divine secret for successful adaptation: "Can anything separate us from the love of Christ? Can trouble, pain or persecution? Can lack of clothes and food, danger to life and limb, the threat of force of arms? Indeed some of us know the truth of that ancient text: 'For Thy sake we are killed all the day long; We were accounted as sheep for the slaughter.' No, in all these things we win an overwhelming victory through Him Who has proved His love for us" (Romans 8:35–37 YOUNG CHURCHES).

Here is the scriptural secret for victorious adaptation to life's insults. At the beginning of each day consider yourself a sheep that is going to be abused even to the extreme of being slaughtered. When you wake up in the morning, take a few minutes to ponder the events of the coming day. Then, think of your bed as an altar, and on that altar sacrifice yourself—possessions, pride, and power—to God. If you take that attitude in the morning, then nothing that comes up during the day should frustrate or disturb you.

A man awaiting death is not disturbed by stress factors that upset other people. His arthritis does not worsen because the taxes on his house were raised; his blood pressure does not increase because his employer laid him off; and his ulcerative colitis doesn't flare up because the stock market went down ten points. The crucified will is not frustrated.

The man who willingly, cheerfully, and daily presents himself as a "living sacrifice" can excellently adapt to the most severe situations and, with Paul, be more than a conqueror (see Romans 8:37).

One may ask, "Isn't it foolish to give up our rights?" Perhaps it is not foolish, since in giving up our rights we improve both our health and happiness. In giving the other fellow a "piece of our mind," we always lose our peace of mind. To the unregenerate man it is unthinkable that he should give in when he is right. He refuses to sacrifice his pride; but in doing so, he sacrifices his health. Not too intelligent a transaction!

Jesus said, "Blessed are the meek: for they shall inherit the earth" (Matthew 5:5 NKJB-NT). Christians must renounce every right of their own and live for the sake of Jesus Christ. As the World War II martyr Dietrich Bonhoeffer wrote and lived: "They will not go to law to defend their rights, or make a scene when they suffer injustice, nor do they insist on their legal rights."[7] We may suffer in this life; but the earth belongs to us. As Dietrich Bonhoeffer declared, "Those who now possess it [the world] by violence and injustice shall lose it, and those who here have utterly renounced it, who were meek to the point of the cross, shall rule the new earth."[8]

Sticking up "for our own rights" calls forth many excess hormones. Much stress and sickness result from our unwillingness to sacrifice "our own rights." Christians must remember that "their right is in the will of their Lord—that and no more."[9] Living by this principle, as Christ did, is "the way of the cross."

As it did for Paul and Bonhoeffer, this path will often lead to persecution in this life. But "the way of the cross" is the only way to spiritual fulfillment and freedom from the diseases caused by negative attitudes and personal indignation.

Chapter Twenty-one

Cope With Hope

 Several years ago, the aging Muhammad Ali staged his final inglorious comeback as a boxer. Out of shape and fighting much younger men, Ali attempted a revolutionary boxing tactic. He covered his face and chest with his arms and allowed his opponent to flail away for many rounds. This "rope a dope" technique sometimes worked. If his opponent tired himself out, Ali sometimes was able to come back and win the fight. However, the fierce beatings took a heavy toll on the body and brain of the former champion.

Many people cope with life's stresses in a similar way. When the stresses of life buffet them, they lay against the ropes of despair and wish that things would get better. They erroneously decide that their opponent, stress, is much too strong for them, so they don't even try to fight back. Psychiatrists have labeled this rope-a-dope type of attitude an *external locus of control.* "Externals" feel that everything that happens to them is controlled by external forces and that their actions do not influence what happens to them. Like pawns in a chess game, externals believe that they are randomly moved about by the players of "luck, chance, fate, or predestination."

Contrasting with the rope-a-dopers are the "cope-with-hopers," people with an *internal locus of control.* "Internals" believe that their own actions have a large influence on what happens to them. If they get fired from a job, internals believe that when they go out to look for a job they will be able to find one. They do not give up; rather, they hope for a brighter future.

Many studies have shown the influence of these opposite attitudes on the health and well-being of a person. Psychologists have shown that internals enjoy their employment more, see more opportunities for occupational advancement, relate better to their fellow workers, and are more satisfied with their lives.[1]

Rather than try to change a stressful situation, externals just despair at the hopelessness of the situation. Because they believe that they are powerless to change their stressful situations, they tend to sense higher levels of stress than others even when exposed to the same stressful events. Externals get more emotionally upset when they undergo severe life stresses, and they are more likely to develop severe emotional disturbances as a result of these stresses.[2]

One of David's patients once came to the hospital with a horrible-smelling ulcer on her breast. One year earlier, her doctors had found a tiny lump that turned out to be a highly treatable breast cancer. However, she had refused medical treatment because God had promised her that He would "heal the cancer." She went to a meeting of a popular faith healer where she was "slain in the Spirit," and the faith healer informed her that she was "healed of her cancer." On this particular visit to the clinic, she just wanted something to get rid of the smell. The cancer, however, had spread throughout her body, and she soon died. If she had initially allowed doctors to treat her cancer, she probably would have lived to see her children grow up. Instead, she died a gruesome death, denying to the end that she had any cancer. She did not realize that God had allowed her doctors to acquire the ability and knowledge to cure her disease. She had confused faith with wishful thinking.

In a similar way, some Christians have been misinformed as to their own responsibility in coping with stress. They have been told that since God predestines everything, they need do nothing because God will handle the stress. They take on an external locus of control; and, thus, expose themselves to the ravages of inner stress. Christians must realize that *the Bible consistently teaches that what we do does make a difference*. We are not God's pawns in some oversized chess game. We are responsible for our actions. Although God empowers and guides our actions, we still must act.

I once heard a story of a man trapped in his home during a raging storm. The water swirled up around his house until he was forced onto the roof. He was not worried, however, for God had promised him that He would rescue him. Soon a boat came by and the rescuers told him to get into the boat. But the man had faith in God and trusted Him to save him. Even when the water forced him onto the chimney this man's faith held firm, and he turned down a ride in a helicopter. This was certainly a stressful situation, but he had the assurance of God that he would be rescued. When he got to heaven, the angels were surprised to see him; for they had even sent *two* rescuers just to make sure that he would be saved!

This story, although apocryphal, illustrates the fact that God has given us many ways to control stress. As Paul wrote, ". . . work out your own salvation with fear and trembling; for it is God who works in you both to will and *to do* for His good pleasure" (Philippians 2:12,13 NKJB-NT, italics added). Faith in God does not preclude action on our part. On the contrary, faith in God results in action.

The most important method for coping with stress is called *control*, which psychologists define as the ability to change or avoid a stressful situation. People who learn how to exert control over stress factors seldom suffer from most stresses.

For example, people who are put in nursing homes often feel that they have lost control of their lives. They often feel that all decisions are made for them and that they have very little to say about what they want. Because of this feeling of having no control, the elderly in institutions often have increased levels of the stress hormone cortisol in their blood. However, if psychologists teach them ways to control stressful situations, their cortisol levels drop rapidly and drastically.[3]

An interesting experiment will serve to further illustrate this point. People were placed in booths and required to do arithmetic problems in their heads. While trying to do these problems, the subjects were exposed to noise. One group of subjects was able to control the volume of noise, but the members of the other group were simply subjected to the volume chosen by a partner in the group with volume control. Thus, both groups were exposed to identical noise volumes; the only difference between the groups was their ability to control the volume of noise. In comparison with the group with volume control, the group that had no control had much higher levels of cortisol in their blood, and they reported that they were much more uncomfortable.[4] Thus, the ability to control external stress has a large influence on how much internal stress we experience.

In order to control stressful situations so that we do not experience large amounts of disease-producing internal stress, we need to practice at least four disciplines:

1. Diversify the stressful agents.
2. Avoid long exposure to stress.
3. Concentrate your efforts on what you can do well.
4. Take a positive attitude.

First: man cannot take long or continued exposure to any one stress factor. The carpenter who pounds nails all day should not spend his evenings spading flower beds, mowing the lawn, or working in his carpentry shop. These activities would be ideal for a clerk or a lawyer.

Failure to diversify the stressful agents will sooner or later result in fatigue, one of the most important symptoms of stress in the body. A number of years ago I saw a diagram in a medical journal that showed how a person can avoid fatigue. The article explained that attention should be given to three angles of life:

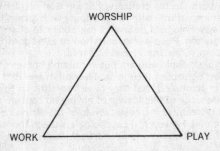

Our society places great emphasis on the bottom two parts of this triangle, but tends to ignore the importance of time spent in worship. We live in a society that works too hard and plays too hard. We say, "Every boy can grow up to be President"; but we forget that the stress of this position often takes a heavy toll on the health of the man who holds it. Our favorite sport is football—a sport that glorifies violence and stressful situations but does little for proper physical fitness.

From my experience I can recall times when I worked so hard during the day that I was tempted not to go to prayer meeting because of my fatigue. Before the prayer meeting ended, however, I was surprised to find that not only had my fatigue gone; but I felt rested and refreshed. Weekly attendance at church services, daily reading of the Bible, and a constant attitude of prayer are of the greatest medicinal value.

In Hebrews 10:25, God commands Christians not to "give up meeting together." In fact, one study done in Maryland found that men who regularly attended church services had a death rate that was 40 percent lower than men who rarely or never went to church. Even more convincing was the death rate of churchgoing women—half of the rate for nonchurchgoers![5] In a society that scoffs and calls religion "the opiate of the masses," modern science has clearly demonstrated that regular church attendance has far more medicinal value than any drug derived from the opium poppy.

Second: avoid long and continued exposure to severe stress agents. There is a limit to the stress that any person can endure. Every physician sees men and women who pay dearly in body and mind for their excessive application to work without proper rest periods. One study found that 26 percent of men who suffered heart attacks had been working over seventy hours a week.[6] Many people would be alive today if they had heeded the admonition of Jesus to His laboring disciples: " 'Come aside by yourselves to a deserted place and rest a while.' For there were many coming and going, and they did not even have time to eat" (Mark 6:31 NKJB-NT).

Just resting is not enough, however. When we withdraw from the cares of this world, we should not seek just to be alone. Rather, we should cultivate quiet fellowship with God: not the despair of empty loneliness but the communion of rich solitude. We must learn to be silent before God and listen to Him. If "Jesus often withdrew to lonely places and prayed" (Luke 5:16 NIV), how can we mere mortals neglect quietly communing with the most high God? As we learn this attitude of solitude, we become able to have peace within our souls even when facing severe stress.

Richard J. Foster writes, "In the midst of noise and confusion we are settled into a deep inner silence."[7] Thus, the Christian uses his rest to draw close to God, and God fills him with a spirit of serenity. This spirit of serenity not only relieves inner stress it prepares the Christian to face future stress.

Third: we experience inner stress whenever we try to do things for which we do not have the ability, the experience, or the time to do well. We need to avoid overextending ourselves.

Remember the first time that you spoke in public, drove a car, or maybe even jumped out of an airplane? When we try to do almost anything for the first time, we experience severe inner stress. But even the parachutist soon gains confidence in his ability and his parachute. With each jump, his level of internal anxiety lowers; and he soon experiences little more stress when walking out of the door of an airplane than when walking through the door of an elevator. Confidence, gained by experience, that we can control a situation lowers our level of internal stress.

We will always be at the mercy of our enemy stress if we do not learn to do things well. We must find what activities our capabilities enable us to do well. As Paul wrote, ". . . each man has his own gift from God; one has this gift, another has that" (1 Corinthians 7:7 NIV). After we discover our capabilities, we can apply ourselves to mastering whatever it is that our capabilities enable us to do. The person who would teach biology should spend much time studying the subject. The person who would hammer nails should practice until he can do it neatly and quickly. The person who would get married should spend much time learning patience and how to give without expecting anything in return.

Fourth: our attitude is the most important factor in determining whether we will suffer from exposure to life's daily stress. We tend to blame our problems on the annoying people around us instead of blaming our troubles on our faulty reactions to those people. The sorrows and insults of daily living need not cause much trouble if we take them with a positive mental attitude. Chronic brooding over sorrows and insults indicates faulty adaption, which can cause any condition from bothersome itchy feet to a fatal heart attack.

Actually, we shouldn't blame an unreasonable boss, teacher, or spouse for our ulcers. Take as an example my telephone, which rings dozens of times while I am trying to paint some lawn furniture. After the first dozen unnecessary interruptions, my natural tendency is to execrate the unobliging callers. Yet I know that if I allow myself to react with antagonism, my impatient reaction might cause my ulcer to flare up. The stresses that hit me are not as culpable as my reaction to them. Most of us have been guilty of generating ten dollars' worth of adrenaline over a ten-cent incident.

In fact, while I was typing the last sentence, my telephone rang. I heard the voice of one of the college infirmary nurses: "Doctor McMillen, there's a girl here with her dog. The dog has a fishhook in its ear. I don't know how to take it out, so I am sending her over to your office."

I can remember a time when my remarks to that nurse might have burned out a wire in the telephone circuit. After all, I'm not the local veterinarian. I also know that if I had reacted with antagonism, I could have experienced a severe, pounding headache—not because of the telephone message but because of my big reaction to the insignificant stress of a simple, humanitarian request. A faulty reaction on my part, instead of giving me a pounding headache, could have given me a stroke or a fatal heart attack. Years ago my faulty adaption to stress nearly caused my death from a bleeding ulcer. In dealing with my ulcer, I became painfully aware of the effect of my reactions on my stomach's secretion of enzymes and acid.

When the girl came over, I took the hook out of her dog's ear; and my reward was not a headache but a grateful girl with her happy dog.

We should remember that, in most cases, stress itself does not cause disease. We all must endure trials, but we seldom need suffer from them. In fact, God uses the daily stresses of our lives to strengthen us. As Paul wrote, ". . . we also rejoice in our sufferings, because we know that suffering produces perseverance; perseverance, character; and character, *hope.* And *hope* does not disappoint us . . .'' (Romans 5:4,5 NIV, italics added). Thus, we see that Christians should not try to avoid something just because it may lead to a stressful situation. A certain amount of stress is a necessary and important part of daily life. In fact, stressful situations can produce hope——the necessary ingredient for coping with stress.

This principle is not just abstract theology, for psychologists now affirm the importance of a certain level of stress. The Forbes continuum of stress (figure 23) shows that people function better at a certain optimal level of stress. A person can suffer from too little or too much stress, but somewhere in between these two extremes lies an optimal level of stress.

Dr. Holger Ursin writes, ''If an individual tries to avoid all challenges and 'stresses' of everyday life, he may decrease his ability to meet these unavoidable challenges. Challenge and stress may be necessary for fitness, both physically and mentally. The absence of

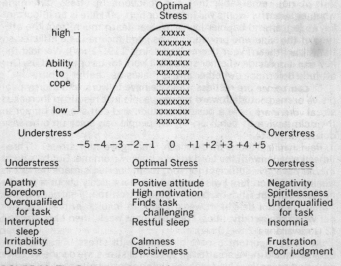

Understress	Optimal Stress	Overstress
Apathy	Positive attitude	Negativity
Boredom	High motivation	Spiritlessness
Overqualified for task	Finds task challenging	Underqualified for task
Interrupted sleep	Restful sleep	Insomnia
Irritability	Calmness	Frustration
Dullness	Decisiveness	Poor judgment

FIGURE 23: The Forbes continuum of stress.

challenge and stress may cause disease, just as overload may produce [disease]."[8]

Each person has a certain optimum level of stress. However, as a person encounters stress, he becomes able to cope with even more stress. Thus, a person who learns how to cope with his current stresses increases his optimal level of stress. Witness the spoiled child who throws his model airplane to the ground as soon as his first attempt at flying the model fails. His parents immediately go out and buy him a new plane, so he does not learn that he handled the stress inappropriately. But the child who has been taught to cope with minor frustrations is not overstressed when his model does not fly. He simply alters the design of the wing or fuselage; and soon he can enjoy watching his plane climb, glide, and swoop across a field.

I can recall many times when I had to make house calls on patients when I wasn't feeling well myself. I found that the stress of making the trip often relieved my minor aches and pains. However, if I had made the trip in the spirit of antagonism, my faulty reaction would have made them even worse.

Is it not remarkable that our reactions to stress determine whether stressful events will help us or hurt us? Here is an important key to longer and happier living. We can learn much from the attitude of the sage who prayed, "It was good for me to be afflicted so that I might learn your decrees" (Psalms 119:71 NIV). We hold the key and can decide whether stress will work for us or against us. Our attitude determines whether stress makes us "better or bitter."

Of course, we are restless when we have to work with thorny people. A wrong attitude toward thorny people just results in increased stress. But if we have a positive attitude and can see the humor in their cantankerous behavior, thorny people can spice up otherwise dull days.

Paul had a "thorn in the flesh" that gave him stress: "Three times I pleaded with the Lord to take it away from me. But he said to me, 'My grace is sufficient for you, for my power is made perfect in weakness.' Therefore I will boast all the more gladly about my weaknesses, so that Christ's power may rest on me. That is why, for Christ's sake, I delight in weaknesses, in insults, in hardships, in persecutions, in difficulties. For when I am weak, then I am strong" (2 Corinthians 12:8–10 NIV).

Another important aspect of coping with stress is called feedback. After we make an attempt to control stress, we decide whether we acted properly. This feedback determines whether we will suffer more stress or feel relief. Consider a pastor who is having a terrible fight with his wife. He may cope with the stress by slamming the door in her face and going to his office to work on his sermon. Soon he feels feedback—guilt and internal stress about his actions. His method of coping with stress has just added more stress. Coping with stress improperly results in increased and sustained internal stress. But if the pastor and his wife sit down together, discuss the disagreement and forgive each other—soon the stressful situation will be over. They will forget their anger and have God's assurance (feedback) that they did the right thing. When we cope with stress properly, we get feedback that enables us to lower our level of internal stress.

As we have seen, people who are unable to cope with external stress suffer much higher levels of internal stress. Thus, these people are much more likely to suffer from diseases that result from stress.

The most important way of coping with stress is control. However, in order to exercise control over stress, we need to believe that we are free to make decisions and that these decisions make a difference in what happens to us. Some humanistic scientists now proclaim that belief in God takes away man's ability to choose—thus, exposing him to unnecessary internal stress. Psychologist Herbert Lefcourt states, "The sense of control, the illusion that one can exercise personal choice, has a definite and a positive role in sustaining life. The illusion of freedom is not to be easily dismissed without anticipating undesirable consequences. To submit to however wise a master planner is to surrender an illusion [freedom of choice] that may be the bedrock on which life flourishes."[9] Dr. Lefcourt has come to the conclusion that submitting to God denies a person free choice. He says that a Christian has given control to God. Since God is in control, he reasons that the Christian is no longer free to exert control over stress.

His argument may make sense at first glance; but because he has never personally experienced the Christian life, he has made an erroneous assumption. He assumes that to surrender to God is to lose the ability to choose. He considers belief in God to be some form of fatalism. Far from it, the Christian is able to choose God's perfect plan for handling stressful situations. The person who has surrendered to God no longer chooses blindly as he did before he came to know God. When we submit to Christ, we do not put on a blindfold and walk into a dark maze of stressful situations. When we come to know Christ, our eyes are opened. Before, we were constantly misled through the maze of life by the prince of darkness; but now we have been transformed so that we are free to choose to follow the God of Light.

Throughout the previous chapters, we have seen how the Bible instructs man in the proper way to handle stress. God does not wish for the Christian to be ignorant of the divine plan for handling human distress. That is why God has so carefully described the proper way for men to control stressful situations. Christians have been freed to follow God's Guidebook for handling stress.

In the boxing ring of life, Christianity is not some spiritual form of rope-a-dope where we lay our trust on the ropes of religion and allow God to pummel us in any way He chooses. God has given us the ultimate, humanistically absurd, promise that ". . . in all things God works for the good of those who love him, who have been called according to his purpose" (Romans 8:28 NIV). No matter how bad things get, Christians need never despair. Christians can always *cope-with-hope.*

Chapter Twenty-two

A Lesson From John D.

In the mid-nineteenth century a strong and husky John D. Rockefeller, Sr., entered the world of business. He drove himself harder than any slave was ever driven by the whip of a taskmaster. At the age of thirty-three, he had made his first million dollars. By dedicating every waking moment to his work, he controlled, at forty-three, the biggest business in the world. By the age of fifty-three, he had become the richest man on earth, the world's only billionaire.

For this achievement, however, he had bartered his own happiness and health. He developed alopecia, a condition in which not only the hair of the head drops out but also most of the hair from the eyelashes and eyebrows. One of his biographers said that he looked like a mummy. His weekly income was a million dollars, but his digestion was so bad that he could eat only crackers and milk.

John D. was as solitary as an oyster. He once confessed that he "wanted to be loved." But he did not understand why people did not seem to love him. Never thinking of others, he had often crushed the helpless in his lust to make bigger profits. So hated was he in the oil fields of Pennsylvania that the men whom he had pauperized hanged him in effigy, and his bodyguards had to watch him day and night. The mass of wealth he had accumulated gave him neither peace nor happiness. In fact, as he sought to protect and control his wealth, he discovered that he was being smothered by it. He could not sleep; he enjoyed nothing.

When John D. was only fifty-three, Ida Tarbell wrote of him, "An awful age was in his face. He was the oldest man that I have ever seen." The crackers and milk he glumly swallowed could no longer hold together his skinny body and restless soul. It was generally agreed that he would not live another year, and newspaper writers had his obituary written and ready in their files.

Then John D. began to do some thinking in the long nights when he couldn't sleep. One night he made a startling discovery: he would not be able to take even one of his thin dimes with him into the next world! His was the despair and helplessness of the little boy who sees the relentless tide coming in to wash into oblivion the sand castles that he has been building.

For the first time in his life he recognized that money was not a commodity to be hoarded but something to be shared for the benefit of others. In the morning, he lost no time in transforming his money into blessings for others. He established the Rockefeller Foundation, so that some of his fortune could be channeled to needed areas. It would require a book to describe the benefits that resulted from the many hundreds of millions of dollars that he showered on universities, hospitals, missions. and millions of underprivileged people. He was the one who helped rid the South of its greatest economic and physical scourge—hookworm. We can thank John D. every time our lives and the lives of our children are saved by an injection of penicillin, because his contributions aided in the discovery of this miracle drug. His money sparked the research that saved and is still saving millions of people from untimely deaths from malaria, tuberculosis, diphtheria, and many other diseases.

It is not my purpose to detail the blessings the world received when John D. changed the direction of his stream of thought from getting to giving. My object is to tell you that when he began to think outwardly toward the needs of others, a miracle occurred. He began to sleep restfully, eat normally, and live joyfully. The bitterness, rancor, and the hollowness of self-centeredness went out of his life, and into John D. flowed refreshing streams of love and gratitude from those whom he was helping. Formerly repulsive and lifeless, he became lovable and vibrant.

When Rockefeller was fifty-three, it certainly appeared that he would never celebrate another birthday, but he started to practice one of God's eternal laws, and he reaped its promised benefits: "Give, and it will be given to you. A good measure, pressed down, shaken together and running over, will be poured into your lap" (Luke 6:38 NIV). He demonstrated the value of this promise: for he survived not only his fifty-fourth and fifty-fifth birthdays, but he experienced "the good measure . . . running over"—living to see his ninety-eighth birthday.

Modern psychiatry is also catching up with the numerous and valuable biblical admonitions to think outwardly in helpfulness toward others. One psychiatrist writes, "Without love, we lose the will to live. Our mental and physical vitality is impaired, our resistance is lowered, and we succumb to illnesses that often prove fatal. We may escape death, but what remains is a meager and barren existence, emotionally so impoverished that we can only be called half alive."[1]

Many of us try to take proper care of our bodies by eating carefully, exercising regularly, and conscientiously following our doctors' orders; but we are sadly ignorant of certain mental exercises that are necessary for full-orbed happy living. Ideally, this training to think outwardly should begin during early childhood. Unfortunately, a one-year-old is often trained to think inwardly and to sense his own importance. Every time he makes the slightest fuss, his parents and grandparents rush to the crib, pick him up, give him a bottle, walk the floor, or do something to let him know that sun, moon, and stars are ready to answer his every cry. Most pediatricians now agree that, by the age of six months, a baby should be left to cry if there is no obvious reason for discomfort and the baby does not appear to be sick.

Many a baby, however, becomes accustomed to having everything rise and set according to his cry; and, with the passing of months and years, he cleverly perfects his technique for keeping the attention of others focused on himself. As a first grader in school, he reports to his parents that a smaller boy called him a "sissy." So when he knocks the boy down and kicks him in the face, the doting father chuckles and applauds, "Good boy!" When the sixth grader wails, "That old principal punished me for nothing at all!" many a parent judges the case on the plea of the juvenile plaintiff.

Parents who everlastingly throw mud at their neighbors' doorsteps in order to make their own look cleaner are setting a vicious example, which their children usually follow. Parents should not blame their children for developing sour personalities, if the dining table becomes an autopsy slab on which the faults of neighbors are exhaustively dissected.

Far too much of our efforts and money is directed inwardly, to build up the egos of our children. We buy eight-year-old Susie expensive designer jeans that she will soon grow out of, the latest video game that she will soon tire of, and the hottest filthy rock album that she soon won't listen to; but we seldom make any worthwhile effort to get her to think about others.

Positive outward thinking is possible, but it takes effort on the part of both parents and children. We can buy Susie a cake mix and have her bake and frost a cake to take to an overworked or sick neighbor. What better investment can a parent make with so little money? Developing an outward pattern of thought will start Susie down the road to joyful living and mental health. Some of the loveliest personalities I know are little children who sacrifice candy money so that they can give to missions and the underprivileged. Children trained early to be considerate of others are not very likely to end up as bitter disappointments to their parents.

The wise father can tell his fourteen-year-old to go to the home of a needy neighbor and mow the lawn, rake the leaves, or shovel the snow. If this kind of self-giving is inculcated into a child, the father won't have to listen to the type of backtalk so common in our society today.

It seems as though parents are going the opposite way when they equip three-year-old Keith with gun belt and six-shooters to "bang bang" at every passing person. Thus, he becomes accustomed to the idea that he can get what he wants by hurting and even killing others.

Because we have allowed and even encouraged the six-month-old baby to be *all lungs*, the ten-year-old child to be *all play*, the teenaged boy to be *all competitive sports*, the teenaged girl to be *all fluffs and frills*, the thirty-five-year-olds *all business or football*, and the forty-five-year-olds *all middle*—is it any wonder that fifty-five-year-olds are *all frustrations*, and the sixty-five-year-olds are *all done*?

John D. Rockefeller showed that we can live healthful, enjoyable lives not by grabbing but by giving to others. When grateful citizens of Cleveland, Ohio, congratulated him, he spoke from his own experience: "Turn your thoughts upon the higher things of life. Be of service to humanity. Turn your thoughts into channels of usefulness; look forward to a determination that something useful shall come out of your success. Let your question be, 'What shall be the fruitage of my career? Shall it be the endowment of hospitals, churches, schools, and asylums?' . . . *Do everything you can for the betterment of your fellow-men and in doing this you will enjoy life the better.*"[2]

For Rockefeller, it took over a half century of sickly, wretched living before he found one of the basic secrets to real living. It is truly pathetic that, as a youth, he did not read and heed the healthful admonitions given in the Bible:

> . . . be generous and willing to share.
> 1 Timothy 6:18 NIV

> And do not forget to do good and to share with others, for with such sacrifices God is pleased.
> Hebrews 13:16 NIV

> One man gives freely, yet gains even more;
>> another withholds unduly, but comes to poverty.
> A generous man will prosper;
>> he who refreshes others will himself be refreshed.
>> Proverbs 11:24,25 NIV

It is not easy for anybody to practice these directives using only his own strength. Modern psychiatry may agree with the Bible in recognizing that thinking outwardly will lead to better mental and physical health, but how can a person begin to think of others if his motivation remains that of self-improvement? It is impossible to develop an outward pattern of thought if we do it to benefit ourselves.

Psychiatry ordinarily cannot provide sufficient motivating force to get any flow past unlovely obstructions—such as the powerful odor in my waiting room one night. It emanated from diapers that had not been properly washed before being put back on a two-month-old baby. The baby's mother, about thirty years old, had given birth to nine babies, and seven of her children were living. She was dirty, slouchy, and impoverished.

I am ashamed to acknowledge the fact, but if it were not for the grace of God in my heart, I would have asked her to look elsewhere for future medical attention. The mental strain of trying to keep such a family healthy under such difficult circumstances was more than I wanted. Why then should I become entangled again with them?

But I did. How could I do otherwise when I remembered how Jesus left the glories of heaven and came to earth because I sorely needed physical, mental, and spiritual help? He came, even though the odor of my sins must have been utterly revolting to His nostrils. The price that He paid to help me could never be measured.

Yes, psychiatry has shown the great importance of thinking outwardly toward other people, but only Christ provides sufficient motivation. He also provides the power: "For whosoever will save his life shall lose it: and whosoever will lose his life for my sake shall find it" (Matthew 16:25 KJV).

". . . for my sake . . ."—there is the power, and there is the motivation that can save us from the deadly sin of self-centeredness.

Chapter Twenty-three

Don't Shoot for the Moon

"Daddy, I want to go to the moon." Those were the words of my three-year-old daughter, Linda, as we sat on our open terrace in Africa. One could hardly blame her, because the big tropical moon looked very, very close and resembled an enthralling fairyland. I carefully and patiently explained to her that the moon was much farther away than it appeared. In fact, no one had yet been able to go there.

Linda's desire to go was so intense that it closed her mind to every word of explanation. She continued to plead excitedly. Exasperated with me, she broke into tears and wept, "Daddy, you don't even try! Go bring the dining table out here. Pile another table on it, and then all the chairs in the house, on the top of each other."

Finally she worked both of us into a lather of mental frenzy. My last words were neither famous nor psychologically outstanding, but they were effective: "Linda, if you don't stop pestering me to take you to the moon, I'll give you a good smackin'!"

When I recall her taut emotions, I can easily understand why strivings for places of eminence, with their consequent frustrations, are potent precipitating factors in the causation of mental disturbances. There are far more than mythical and etymological connections between *lunar* strivings and *lunacy*.

Arlene was a college senior and had been on the dean's list from

193

the time she was a freshman, a feat somewhat comparable to going to the moon. She gloated over seeing her name in that coveted column, but in her senior year she began to feel herself slipping. The thought of not achieving her goal made her anxious, panicky, and decreased her ability to concentrate on her studies. She worried even though she had already been accepted at a prestigious law school, so her grades were of little significance to her future career.

Then one day Arlene entered the infirmary because she couldn't read. She could pronounce words but could not understand what they meant. A week passed, with little improvement. Each day increased her anxiety because it lessened her chances of corralling those elusive A's.

She was sure there was something physically wrong with her. Even though I told her that she needed a changed viewpoint about striving for the moon, she continued to worry about her falling grades. She returned to her hometown, where she was thoroughly examined in a hospital. She emerged with a large bill and a diagnosis of "somatic conversion disorder," which means in five-cent words that her inability to read was caused by mental turmoil. Anxiety about her grades had manifested itself by a withdrawal symptom—an inability to read. Because she was unable to graduate with her class, she also lost her place in law school.

Psychic turmoil, arising out of our desires to go to the moon or to attain superiority over our fellows, is very common. An outstanding psychiatrist, Dr. Alfred Adler, taught that most modern nervous and emotional disorders grow out of a definite striving for power. Because the average man in his mad drive for power is in a daily race with others for earthly goals, his day is full of botched-up tasks, pent-up frustrations, banged-up feelings, and often, banged-up fenders.

The next time you feel unduly fatigued because life's race has been unusually rough and bumpy, stop and analyze the events and conversation of the preceding hours. Ninety-nine times out of a hundred you will discover that someone recently let the air out of your ego. We suffer rough going, mental weariness, and debilitating disease not because of the work we do; but because we consciously or subconsciously try to prove to ourselves and to our peers that our ideas are superior, our doctrines are correct, our church is the best, our city is the choicest, our state is the most important, our political ideology is necessary to save the world from destruction, or our ball team is going to win the world series. Our, our, our—you name it, and we will argue until we are blue in the face that we are the people and that at our demise wisdom will surely vanish from the earth. It is a wonder that we don't more often blow a cerebral fuse.

Once a young man came to my office with a large hemorrhage in his eye. Nobody had punched him. The blood vessel in his eye had broken because he developed too much blood pressure while playing the high soprano parts on his horn. Remember that young man the next time you feel pressured "to toot your own horn."

Is it not a pity that we are cursed with an innate urge to be ever madly racing with one another like the participants in a stock-car race? In our excitement to be first we become oblivious to the damage we inflict on others and ourselves. The stock cars that are battered, banged, dented, and noisy are no worse off than bruised humanity broken down with many a disease from life's competition. Here are only a few of many New Testament admonitions—or, more accurately, prescriptions—that would save millions of crushed and broken hearts if people had enough faith to assimilate them into their self-concept:

> Don't cherish exaggerated ideas of yourself or your importance, but try to have a sane estimate of your capabilities. . . .
>
> Romans 12:3 YOUNG CHURCHES

> Love must be sincere. . . . Be devoted to one another in brotherly love. Honor one another above yourselves. Live in harmony with one another. Do not be proud, but be willing to associate with people of low position. Do not be conceited.
>
> Romans 12:9,10,16 NIV

> Live together in harmony, live together in love, as though you had only one mind and one spirit between you. Never act from motives of rivalry or personal vanity, but in humility think more of each other than you do of yourselves.
>
> Philippians 2:2,3 YOUNG CHURCHES

Before the disciples had crucified their urge for power, which Dr. Adler calls the "ego ambition," their main drive had been to sit in places of authority and prominence and to be the greatest in the Kingdom. Speaking of the Pharisees and scribes, Jesus said:

> They increase the size of their phylacteries and lengthen the tassels of their robes; they love seats of honour at dinner parties and front places in the synagogues. They love to be greeted with respect in public places and to have men call them "rabbi!" Don't you ever be called "rabbi"—you have only one teacher, and all of you are

brothers. . . . And you must not let people call you "leaders"—you have only one leader, Christ! The only "superior" among you is the one who serves the others. For
every man who promotes himself will be humbled, and
every man who learns to be humble will find promotion.

Matthew 23:5–12 PHILLIPS

This scriptural teaching is diametrically opposed to the philoso-
phies of the world. Jesus very forcibly warns us against aspiring to
leadership. His teaching does not give us any excuse for laziness but
rather exhorts that we give proper motivation and direction to expending our energies. Expending our energies may be compared to
expending nuclear energy: *undirected* expenditure of nuclear energy
is a horror-producing bomb; *directed* expenditure of nuclear energy
is a power-generating plant. We must allow Christ to direct our
goals. The teaching of Jesus translated into college language is
don't get your heart set on being a "four pointer" or being on the
dean's list; don't lose sleep over being selected homecoming queen;
don't strive to be the leader of any class, any committee, or anything else. Graduate work may be necessary, but don't do it to
"lengthen the tassel" on the end of your name. In God's Book, the
only "superior" among us is the one who serves the others.

Going back to medical considerations, you may wonder why the
individual working to be a four-pointer suffers in his body and mind
while another student, working just as hard and doing just as well, is
free from such injuries. The student who is striving for the coveted
A's and for the preeminence they will give him is actually digging a
channel to direct the current of interests toward himself. His ego-
centric life, with no outflow, will be bitter and senseless. He will suffer from self-intoxication. He who refuses the biblical injunction to
adjust himself to "humble situations" will soon discover that his associates will take it upon themselves to make the necessary adjustments to him in a fashion that may be crude and heartless. The
stress he then suffers can cause plenty of trouble in mind and body.

In contrast, the individual who practices God's Word is spared
many bodily insults. The psalmist wrote, "Great peace have they
who love your law, and nothing can make them stumble" (Psalms
119:165 NIV). Nothing? I can't imagine greater stress than being
thrown into fire; yet the Bible tells of three men who were thrown
into an inferno, and they emerged without even the smell of smoke
on their garments.

Everybody meets frustration every day, but the Christian need
never become frustrated. A number of times I have seen Stephen W.
Paine face frustrating and personally embarrassing situations as a

college president. Each time I was refreshed when he said, "It is perfectly all right. Perhaps the Lord sent it to keep me humble."

There is another big difference between the individual who is seeking great things for himself and the one whose energies are devoted to God's Kingdom. In our world of business the individual who is self-employed has only his own resources to fall back upon when he meets trouble. But the man who is a vital part of a large corporation has all the resources of a billion-dollar company. Hence, he has a sense of security in knowing that, regardless of what happens, his corporation is not likely to go bankrupt. So is the man who is faithfully devoting his energies to the business of the King who owns the cattle on a thousand hills, the oil in a million wells, and the silver, gold, and jewels in a billion solar systems. With his position in the business of this King comes the security of absolutely guaranteed eternal life insurance. Not only is he free from worries, insults, and antagonisms incident to self-seeking; but he can have a pleasing personality, denied to those who shoot for the moon.

Some time ago I read about a young woman who wanted to go to college. Her heart sank when she read one question on the application blank: "Are you a leader?" Being a conscientious girl she wrote "No" and sent in the form, but she was sure that she did not have a chance. To her surprise she received a letter from one of the college officials, which read something like this: "A study of the application blanks reveals that this year our college will have 1452 leaders. Therefore, we are accepting you because we feel it is imperative that they have at least one follower."

It is easy to find people who want to be head cook, but few are willing to wash dishes. There are always several hundreds of girls who yearn to ride in the parade as the beautiful queen, but often only a disgruntled half dozen show up to decorate the float. Construction crews never lack those who want to be job foreman, but they have to search for men to drive nails and saw boards.

Medical statistics show that the whistling ditchdigger is less likely to buy his tombstone from the distraught business manager than he is to dig the businessman's grave. Maybe, in our striving for the moon, we aren't too smart, after all. I grant you, it must be a thrill to shoot for the moon in an upholstered space capsule. Yet, those original capsules bear an uncanny similarity to an asylum's padded cell.

Jesus said something that few people ever took seriously. He said, "The meek . . . shall inherit the earth" (Matthew 5:5 KJV). We can believe that the meek will inherit heaven when they die, but Jesus also meant that the meek are going to inherit the earth here and now. Study the meek people you know, and you will discover that they are actually coming into possession of everything that is worthwhile on this earth. Here is one of their prayers, seasoned with a bit of irony:

> Lord
> keep me from becoming verbose and
> possessed with the idea
> that I must express myself on every subject.
> Release me from the craving
> to straighten out everyone's affairs.
> Teach me the glorious lesson that
> occasionally I may be wrong.
> Make me helpful but
> not bossy.
> With my vast store of wisdom and experience,
> it does seem a pity
> not to use it all—
> But you know,
> Lord,
> that I want a few friends at the end.
> Amen.

Jesus said, "The meek . . . shall inherit the earth." Benito Mussolini and Adolf Hitler didn't believe that, for they attempted to take the earth by force. No one ever lived unhappier lives or died more despicable deaths than they did.

How are we going to take care of this inner power urge, "the ego ambition"? Dr. Adler sought to appease this strong egotistical power urge so that it might work together with the widely different feelings of altruism that man also possesses. To this end he urged his patients to follow the Golden Rule: "In everything, do to others what you would have them do to you" (Matthew 7:12 NIV).

The weakness of the Adler plan was that he was looking only at man's deviant power drive, which is only one symptom of our carnal nature. Freudian thought is similarly flawed in that it centers solely on another outstanding carnal symptom—man's deviant sexual drive. The trouble with both Adler and Freud lies in their treating merely *symptoms* of the carnal nature instead of directing therapy at the *cause*. When a person is dying of meningitis, it helps little to treat the symptoms of headache and fever with some aspirin. The doctor must use antibiotics to attack the cause—the evil infection itself.

The Bible focuses therapy on the cause of the symptoms—the carnal nature: "Those who belong to Christ Jesus have crucified the lower nature with its passions and desires . . ." (Galatians 5:24 NEB).

Instead of making frequent, expensive, and often futile trips to a psychiatrist's couch, we are invited by Christ to come to the cross to crucify our wills. "While Christ was actually taking upon Himself the sins of men, God condemned that sinful nature" (Romans 8:3 YOUNG CHURCHES). When we drive His spikes into everything in our lives that God has marked for destruction, then God, for the sake of Christ, executes that old self which ever breathes out "ego ambition" and lustful attitudes.

"Jesus also suffered outside the city gate to make the people holy through his own blood. Let us, then, go to him outside the camp, bearing the disgrace he bore" (Hebrews 13:12,13 NIV). If you go outside the gate, beyond the opinions and doctrines of man, and allow Him to crucify that disease maker, the old self, you will be able to say with Paul, "I am crucified with Christ: nevertheless I live; yet not I but Christ liveth in me . . ." (Galatians 2:20 KJV).

Chapter Twenty-four

"Two Souls, Alas, Dwell in My Breast Apart"

 On a summer evening some years ago, Joseph Ransler went to the home of his brother, who was away working on a night shift. He visited with his brother's wife, who, he later reported, "was dressed in shorts and a bra, like she always was." A few hours later, Joseph raped his sister-in-law; and to cover up his crime, he strangled the woman and her little daughter. Joseph's brother found their lifeless bodies when he returned home from work.

After seven hours of questioning by the police, Joseph Ransler confessed and made this statement: "What makes a guy act like I do? I want to pray and everything, and inwardly I feel that I want to be the best Christian in the world. But outwardly I'm a maniac and I can't control the outward part. I don't know why." He hadn't made much headway following the inward voice, for the police had previously arrested him a half-dozen times.

He did recognize, however, that within his mind there was a battle between two forces—one for the good and one for the bad. Sigmund Freud recognized the active conflict that occurs in a man's mind. In fact, the Freudian school of psychoanalysis believes that this psychological conflict is the source of most of man's psychic disorders.

Dr. Karl Menninger recognized the existence of these two inner

forces and referred to them as the "life instinct" and "death instinct." The life instinct of a man seeks to preserve life, both his own
and others, while the death instinct seeks to destroy life. People
standing near the brink of a deep canyon often sense an inner agent
that wants to push them over the edge. But they also sense and
usually heed another agent that urges them to step back.

Because the strong evil agent that dwells in man seeks his destruction, it is not surprising that in the United States suicide is the
tenth leading cause of death and the third most common cause of
death among young adults. Annually, over twenty-seven thousand
Americans take their own lives—not to mention the many who dis-
guise their suicides successfully as accidents and the many other
thousands who attempt suicide but fail.

Carl Jung, the founder of the school of analytical psychology, also
was impressed by the fact that neuroses were caused by the battle
between two warring psychological agents. "The conflict may be between the sensual and the spiritual man. . . . It is what Faust means
when he says, 'Two souls, alas, dwell in my breast'. . . . A neurosis is
a dissociation of personality. Healing may be called a religious problem."[1]

Robert Louis Stevenson, in *Dr. Jekyll and Mr. Hyde,* gave a fascinating description of an individual who was swayed one moment by
the beneficent Dr. Jekyll in his nature, and then the next minute he
was turned into and controlled by his evil and murderous Mr. Hyde
nature.

Modern psychologists and psychiatrists have tried to answer the
question of the sex murderer Joseph Ransler, "What makes a guy
act like I do?" Many other people sense their ambivalence—the
presence of two inner forces, one good and one bad. With a little in-
trospection, each of us can sense the presence of two opposite
forces within, especially when we have a moral issue to decide. In the
back of our minds a little creature always encourages us to tell a
"little white lie" since "everybody does it." We often must recognize
the greater power of the evil agent. Although we haven't had to hang
by the neck for our misdeeds, many times we have had to hang our
faces in shame.

Four thousand years before psychiatry awoke to the importance
of two forces within man, God described this conflict in a drama recorded in Genesis.[2] To Abraham and his wife Sarah, God had promised a son through whom all the nations of earth would be blessed.
With the passing of many years, Sarah became so old that she
thought God had forgotten His promise. She decided to help God out
by lending her slave girl Hagar to Abraham so that he might have the
promised heir whose posterity would be as innumerable as the stars
in the sky. Abraham consented to this human scheme without con-

sulting God. In due time, the slave girl bore Abraham a son and called him Ishmael.

Abraham was elated because he had a son and an heir. Now God could use Ishmael to fulfill the divine purpose. Holding Ishmael on his knee, the aged patriarch must have felt strong affection for his only child.

When Ishmael was thirteen years old, God shocked the blissful Abraham by telling him that Ishmael would not be the one through whom He would bless the world. God told Abraham that his shrunken, ninety-year-old wife, Sarah, was going to bear him a son through whom the promise would be fulfilled. The idea of setting aside Ishmael, his firstborn son, greatly disturbed Abraham, who implored God, "If only Ishmael might live under your blessing!" (Genesis 17:18 NIV).

When Abraham finally recognized that God would not change, he accepted the divine plan. By faith a son, Isaac, was miraculously born to the aged Abraham and Sarah.

As the years passed, the conflict between the two basically different sons and women of Abraham became intense, bitter, and murderous. The bickering appeals of his sons—Ishmael, the "wild donkey of a man" in whom lived a spirit of "hostility toward all his brothers" (see Genesis 16:12) and Isaac, the son of miraculous blessing through whom all the nations of the earth would be blessed—tore at Abraham's heart. Just as Ransler, the sex murderer, sensed both the good and the bad forces within himself, Abraham was very conscious of these two diametrically opposed forces under his roof.

When Sarah demanded that Abraham disinherit Ishmael, Abraham became very distressed. But God saw the murderous hatred in Ishmael's heart, so He told Abraham to cast Ishmael out of his house. Cast out his firstborn, his seventeen-year-old son? This command must have saddened Abraham, but by faith he obeyed God. It was better to shed a few tears over Ishmael's dismissal than to shed many more over the murder of Isaac, the son of promise. Let us not forget that the tears Abraham shed over Ishmael were the result of his getting outside God's will. If he had not tried to do things in his own way, he could have avoided all of this trouble.

Paul tells us that these two sons of Abraham were symbolical of the two natures within carnal man:

> Now you, brothers, like Isaac, are children of promise. At that time the son born in the ordinary way persecuted the son born by the power of the Spirit. It is the same now. But what does the Scripture say? "Get rid of the slave woman and her son, for the slave woman's son will

never share in the inheritance with the free woman's son.'' Therefore, brothers, we are not children of the slave woman, but of the free woman.

For the sinful nature desires what is contrary to the Spirit, and the Spirit what is contrary to the sinful nature. They are in conflict with each other, so that you do not do what you want.

Galatians 4:28–31; 5:17 NIV

In writing to the Romans, Paul talked of two warring forces within his own mind. Nineteen centuries before the birth of psychiatry, he dramatically describes the natural state where man is controlled by the greater power of the carnal force:

My own behaviour baffles me. For I find myself not doing what I really want to do but doing what I really loathe. Yet surely if I do things that I really don't want to do it cannot be said that "I" am doing them at all—it must be sin that has made its home in my nature. (And indeed, I know from experience that the carnal side of my being can scarcely be called the home of good!) I often find that I have the will to do good, but not the power. That is, I don't accomplish the good I set out to do, and the evil I don't really want to do I find I am always doing. Yet if I do things that I don't really want to do then it is not, I repeat, "I" who do them, but the sin which has made its home within me. When I come up against the Law I want to do good, but in practice I do evil. My conscious mind whole-heartedly endorses the Law, yet I observe an entirely different principle at work in my nature. This is in continual conflict with my conscious attitude, and makes me an unwilling prisoner to the law of sin and death. In my mind I am God's willing servant, but in my own nature I am bound fast, as I say, to the law of sin and death. It is an agonising situation, and who on earth can set me free from the clutches of my own sinful nature?

Romans 7:15–24 YOUNG CHURCHES

Here is the greatest human question of all time. Abraham, the Apostle Paul, and the sex murderer Ransler faced it. Everyone must look for the answers to many of life's dilemmas; but none is as important as this one: "Who on earth can set me free from the clutches of my own sinful nature?" If one fails here, he will, in a sense, fail in every day that he lives.

There is no lack of answers. Every school of psychiatric thought has a different one—pretty good evidence that none is truly effective. Furthermore, these various schools concern themselves with merely treating symptoms. But there is a cure for mankind's agonizing situation.

Chapter Twenty-five

Freedom From an Agonizing Situation

"Who on earth can set me free from the clutches of my own sinful nature?" Millions of people today ask this same question raised long ago by the Apostle Paul. It was the question that troubled two psychiatrists—husband and wife—as they consulted in their Chicago offices. They were discussing the best way to free a patient from a serious psychological problem.

Dr. Lena Sadler had asked her husband, Dr. William S. Sadler, to see one of her patients, a "refined, highly educated" woman. The patient did not respond, even after their combined psychiatric counseling. Dr. William Sadler advised his wife that this patient would not get much better until her "mental life was set in order and numerous psychic slivers were removed." To the question of how long he thought that would take, he replied, "Probably a year or more."

Dr. William Sadler tells us what happened:

> Imagine my surprise when this patient walked into my office a few days later and informed me that her "troubles were all over," that the things she had assured me a few days previously she "could never do," had all been done, that everything I had asked her to do as part of her

"cure" had been set in operation——she had completely
overhauled her social, family, and personal life, had
made numerous "confessions," and had accomplished a
score of almost impossible mental and "moral" stunts.

In reply to my astonished question, "How in the world
did you ever do all this and effect this great change in
your mental attitude toward yourself and the world in less
than one week?" she smilingly replied, "Dr. Lena taught
me to pray."[1]

Without further long, expensive sessions in a psychiatrist's office,
the woman had confessed her sins to God and to others. Then she
experienced immediately the healing and refreshment of the promise of Jesus: "Peace I leave with you, my peace I give unto you: not
as the world giveth, give I unto you. Let not your heart be troubled,
neither let it be afraid" (John 14:27 KJV).

Dr. Carl Jung also recognized the importance of God in healing
the ills of mankind:

During the past thirty years, people from all the civilized countries of the earth have consulted me. I have
treated many hundreds of patients. . . . Among all my
patients in the second half of life—that is to say, over
thirty-five—there has not been one whose problem in the
last resort was not that of finding a religious outlook on
life. . . .

It seems to me, that, side by side with the decline of
religious life, the neuroses grow noticeably more frequent. . . .

The patient is looking for something that will take possession of him and give meaning and form to the confusion of his neurotic mind. Is the doctor equal to the task?
To begin with, he will probably hand over his patient to
the clergyman or the philosopher, or abandon him to that
perplexity which is the special note of our day. . . .
Human thought cannot conceive any system or final
truth that could give the patient what he needs in order to
live: that is faith, hope, love, and insight. . . .

There are however persons who, while well aware of
the psychic nature of their complaint, nevertheless refuse to turn to the clergyman. They do not believe that he
can really help them. Such persons distrust the doctor for
the same reason, and they are justified by the fact that
both doctor and clergyman stand before them with
empty hands, if not——what is even worse——with empty

words. . . . It is from the clergyman, not from the doctor, that the sufferers should expect such help.[2]

Freud, Adler, and Jung largely agreed that many of man's mental disturbances are due to conflict between inner good and evil forces. Freud emphasized the sexual propensities of the bad force, Adler stressed the ruthless drive of the carnal nature for power and supremacy, while Jung likened the evil part of man to a wild, ravenous wolf.

As early as the 1930s, physicians began to learn that many physical diseases are caused by envy, jealousy, self-centeredness, resentment, fear, and hatred—the identical emotions that the Bible lists as attributes of our carnal nature. Most of the mental and physical ills of man are caused by the activities of an inner evil force. We can understand why human ideas are so ineffective at freeing man from his innate evil nature, for it is as much a part of him as a shell is of a turtle.

Paul recognized his dilemma: "What a wretched man I am! Who will rescue me from this body of death?" (Romans 7:24 NIV). But Paul had found the humanly impossible answer:

> I thank God there *is* a way out through Jesus Christ our Lord. . . . *while Christ was actually taking upon Himself the sins of men, God condemned that sinful nature.* So that . . . we are living no longer by the dictates of our sinful nature, but in obedience to the promptings of the Spirit. . . . Now if Christ does live within you His presence means that your sinful nature is dead. . . .
> Romans 7:25; 8:3,4,10 YOUNG CHURCHES

By His death and resurrection Jesus did not automatically deliver all men from bondage to their lower natures. He made this freedom available only to those who walk in His Spirit. Empowered by God, Spirit-filled Christians can obey the divine conditions:

> Those who belong to Christ Jesus have crucified the sinful nature with its passions and desires.
> Galatians 5:24 NIV

> You must put to death, then, the earthly desires at work in you, such as sexual immorality, indecency, lust, evil passions, and greed (for greed is a form of idolatry). . . . At one time you yourselves used to live according to such desires, when your life was dominated by them. But now you must get rid of all these things: anger, passion, and hateful feelings. No insults or obscene talk must ever

come from your lips. Do not lie to one another, for you
have put off the old self with its habits, and have put on
the new self. This is the new being which God, its Creator,
is constantly renewing in his own image, in order to bring
you to a full knowledge of himself.

Colossians 3:5,7–10 TEV

If . . . you cut the nerve of your instinctive actions by
obeying the Spirit, you are on the way to real living.

Romans 8:13 YOUNG CHURCHES

Billy Graham expresses well the part we must play: "It is only
when we come to the will that we find the very heart of repentance.
There must be that determination to forsake sin—to change one's
attitude toward self, toward sin, and God; to change one's feelings:
to change one's will, disposition, and purpose. . . . There is not one
verse of Scripture that indicates you can be a Christian and live any
kind of a life you want to."[3]

Remember, Paul said that the two warring factions of Abraham's
family symbolized the two forces, struggling to control our wills.[4]
But Paul made the application for us: "Get rid of the slave woman
and her son" (Galatians 4:30 NIV). It will give us pain to say farewell
to the carnal part of our natures, which has given us a large share of
life's so-called pleasures. It will mean giving up some of our habits,
our friends, our practices, and our thought patterns.

Letting go of these "pleasures" may give us much sorrow at the
time. Yet it is not a dismissal of worthwhile joys and friends but of
those born, like Ishmael, outside of God's will for our lives. " 'I
promise you,' " returned Jesus, 'that nobody has left home or
brothers or sisters or mother or father or children or land for my
sake and the gospel's without getting back a hundred times over,
now in this present life . . . and in the next world eternal life' " (Mark
10:30,31 PHILLIPS).

Jesus recognizes that we will feel some pain in giving up our carnal pleasures, but He promises that we will receive, here "in this
present life," "a hundred times" as much of the worthwhile. His
statement is partly understandable when we realize the vast array of
mental and physical diseases from which we are freed when we, with
God's help, cast out the innate troublemaker.

We may shed some tears in saying farewell to the old life and its
lure, but our grief will seem inconsequential moments later when we
experience the exhilaration of His resurrection, life, and power
within us: "If we have been united with him in his death, we will certainly also be united with him in his resurrection. For we know that
our old self was crucified with him so that the body of sin might be

rendered powerless, that we should no longer be slaves to sin"
(Romans 6:5,6 NIV).

Surrendering one's will to the divine will may seem a negative
procedure, but it gives many positive dividends. Psychologist Wallace Emerson writes, "It is a will that, while giving up the mastery,
has finally become something of a master in its own house."[5]

By now you may agree that to follow the commandments of the
Bible is the only way to true "wholistic" health. But don't make the
mistake of an elderly woman who responded to one of my sermons,
"Doctor, I've been sick for many years, and I want to get well. Starting today, I'm going to obey the Bible. It must be worth it, to feel
better."

She had it all backward. Sure, following the teachings of Christ is
the way to fulfilled living and improved health; but to live for Jesus
solely for the sake of better health just enslaves our carnal natures
to one more idol—the idol of better health. Living according to biblical commandments will, of course, improve the health of both those
who know Christ and those who do not. This point is aptly demonstrated by the followers of pseudo-christian cults who enjoy improved health because they follow many of the teachings of Christ,
but they deny the deity of Christ. If your ultimate goal is better
health, however, you can never be a true follower of Jesus Christ.

Christianity that exists solely to make us healthy is a hollow religion that leaves us spiritually dead. Seeking our own good we again
fall prey to that demon, self.

But following Christ can mean so much more. As we crucify our
wills and as we become slaves to righteousness, we can begin to
drink of the water that eternally satisfies our most basic thirst—our
need to know God. Jesus said, "Whoever drinks of the water that I
shall give him will never thirst. But the water that I shall give him will
become in him a fountain of water springing up into everlasting life"
(John 4:14 NKJB-NT).

A. W. Tozer writes, "The Bible is not an end in itself, but a means
to bring men to an intimate and satisfying knowledge of God, that
they may enter into Him, that they may delight in His Presence, may
taste and know the inner sweetness of the very God Himself in the
core and center of their hearts."[6]

As we so worship Christ, He allows us to experience the *transforming power* of His Spirit. Richard J. Foster declares, "To stand
before the Holy One of eternity is to change. Resentments cannot be
held with the same tenacity when we enter His gracious light. . . . In
worship an increased power steals its way into the heart sanctuary,
an increased compassion grows in the soul. To worship is to
change."[7]

Worshiping the Creator of the universe, we become *transformed*.

God enables us to *crucify* the inner troublemaker so that Christ may rule in the throne room of our wills. Only then do we begin to experience real living, renewed vitality, inner peace, impassioned spirituality, exuberant joy, and the fullness of God's promise, *"none of these diseases."*

Source Notes

Chapter 1

1. S. E. Massengill, *A Sketch of Medicine and Pharmacy* (Bristol, Tenn.: S. E. Massengill Co., 1943), p. 16.
2. *Ibid.*
3. *Scope* (Summer 1955), p. 13.
4. C. P. Bryan, *The Papyrus Ebers* (London: Geoffrey Bles, 1930).
5. Acts 7:22, NIV.
6. George Rosen, *History of Public Health* (New York: MD Publications, 1958), pp. 62–63.
7. *Ibid.*, pp. 63–65.
8. Arturo Castiglione, *A History of Medicine* (New York: Alfred A. Knopf, Inc., 1941), p. 71.
9. Th. M. Vogelsang, "Leprosy in Norway," *Medical History* 9 (1965):31.
10. J. C. Pedley, *Leprosy Review* 41 (1970):167.

Chapter 2

1. Arturo Castiglione, *A History of Medicine* (New York: Alfred A. Knopf, Inc., 1941), p. 70.
2. Walter J. Hierholzer, Jr., "Nosocomial Bacterial Infections," in *Bacterial Infections of Humans: Epidemiology and Control,* ed. A. S. Evans and H. A. Feldman (New York: Plenum Publishing Co., 1982), p. 383.
3. Numbers 19.
4. A. C. Steere and G. F. Mallison, *Annals of Internal Medicine* 83 (1975):685.
5. *Ibid.*
6. *An Epitome of the History of Medicine,* 2nd ed. (Philadelphia: F. A. Davis Co., 1901), p. 326.
7. F. Daschner, H. Nadjem, H. Langmaak and W. Sandritter, *Infection* 6 (1978):261.
8. John P. Burke et al., "*Proteus mirabilis* Infections in a Hospital Nursery Traced to a Human Carrier," *New England Journal of Medicine* 284 (1971):115.

Chapter 3

1. Secretary of Health and Human Services, *Fourth Special Report to the U.S. Congress on Alcohol and Health* (Washington, D.C.: Government Printing Office, 1981).
2. U.S., Department of Health and Human Services, *First Statistical Compendium on Alcohol and Health* (Washington, D.C.: Government Printing Office, 1981).
3. A. Medhus, "Mortality Among Female Alcoholics," *Scandinavian Journal of Social Medicine* 3 (1975):111.

4. Othello, II. iii. 283.
5. Macbeth, II. iii. 34.
6. R. J. Sokol, S. I. Miller, and G. Reed, "Alcohol Abuse During Pregnancy," *Alcoholism* 4 (1980):135–145.
7. "A Problem in Business and Industry," Yale Center of Alcohol Studies, p. 251.
8. R. E. Berry, Jr., et al., *The Economic Costs of Alcohol Abuse and Alcoholism* (Brookline, Mass.: Policy Analysis, Inc., 1977).
9. Donald W. Goodwin, "Genetic Component of Alcoholism," *Annual Review of Medicine* 32 (1981):93–99.

Chapter 4

1. E. Silverberg and J. A. Lubera, "A Review of American Cancer Society Estimates of Cancer Cases and Deaths," *Ca—A Cancer Journal for Clinicians* 33 (1983):15. © 1983 American Cancer Society, Inc.
2. Alton Ochsner, *Smoking and Cancer* (New York: Julian Messner, Inc., 1954), p. 12.
3. *Ibid.*, p. 4.
4. G. Hammond and L. Garfinkel, "General Air Pollution and Cancer in the United States," *Preventive Medicine* 9 (1980):206.
5. Surgeon General, *The Health Consequences of Smoking: Cancer* (Washington, D.C.: Government Printing Office, 1981).
6. Surgeon General, *Smoking and Health* (Washington, D.C.: Government Printing Office, 1979).
7. Surgeon General, *Health Consequences of Smoking: Cancer,* pp. 41, 69.
8. *Ibid.*, pp. 111, 129; Surgeon General, *Smoking and Health,* chap. 4, p. 30; chap. 4, p. 49.
9. O. Auerbach et al., "Cigarette Smoking and Coronary Artery Disease," *Chest* 70 (1976):699.
10. Surgeon General, *Smoking and Health,* chap. 4, p. 51.
11. The Pooling Research Group, *Journal of Chronic Diseases* 31 (1978):201.
12. N. L. Benowitz et al., "Smokers of Low-Yield Cigarettes Do Not Consume Less Nicotine," *New England Journal of Medicine* 309 (1983):139; J. H. Jaffe et al., "Carbon Monoxide and Thiocyanate Levels in Low Tar/Nicotine Smokers," *Addictive Behaviors* 6 (1981):337.
13. D. W. Kaufman et al., "Nicotine and Carbon Monoxide Content of Cigarette Smoke and the Risk of Myocardial Infarction in Young Men," *New England Journal of Medicine* 308 (1983):409.
14. Surgeon General, *The Health Consequences of Smoking for Women* (Washington, D.C.: Government Printing Office, 1980), p. 162.
15. H. W. Daniell, "Smokers Wrinkles: A Study in the Epidemiology of 'Crow's Feet,' " *Annals of Internal Medicine* 75 (1971): 873.
16. C. Schirren, *Geburtshilfe und Frauenheilkunde* 35 (1975):334.
17. M. A. Russel, P. V. Cole and E. Brown, "Absorption by Non-smokers of Carbon Monoxide from Room Air Polluted by Tobacco Smoke," *Lancet* 1 (1973):576.
18. Surgeon General, *Health Consequences of Smoking: Cancer,* p. 214.
19. T. Hirayama, *British Medical Journal* 283 (October 3, 1983):916.
20. B. R. Luce and S. O. Schweitzer, "The Economic Costs of Smoking Induced

Illness," in *Research in Smoking Behavior*, ed. M. E. Jarvick et al. (Washington, D.C.: Government Printing Office, 1977), pp. 221–229.

21. Adapted from Silverberg and Lubera, "A Review of American Cancer Society Estimates of Cancer Cases and Deaths," p. 14. © 1983 American Cancer Society, Inc.

22. Surgeon General, *Smoking and Health*, p. 60.

23. Surgeon General, *Health Consequences of Smoking for Women*, p. 192.

24. J. Goujard, C. Rumeau and D. Schwartz, "Smoking During Pregnancy: Stillbirth and Abruptio Placentae," *Biomedicine* 23 (1975):20–22.

25. J. Andrews and J. M. McGarry, "A Community Study of Smoking in Pregnancy," *Journal of Obstetrics and Gynecology of the British Commonwealth* 79 (1972):1057.

26. N. R. Butler and H. Goldstein, "Smoking in Pregnancy and Subsequent Child Development," *British Medical Journal* 4 (1973):573.

27. R. I. Evans and A. Henderson, "Smoking in Children and Adolescents: Psychosocial Determinants and Prevention Strategies," in *The Behavioral Aspects of Smoking*, ed. N. A. Krasnegor (Washington, D.C.: Government Printing Office, 1976), pp. 69–96.

28. B. Mausner and E. S. Platt, *Smoking: A Behavioral Analysis* (New York: Pergamon Press, 1971).

29. *Report of the Task Force on Tobacco and Cancer, Target 5* (New York: American Cancer Society, Inc., 1976).

30. Butler and Goldstein, "Smoking in Pregnancy and Subsequent Child Development," p. 201.

31. J. L. Hamilton, *Review of Economics and Statistics* 54 (1972):401.

32. Surgeon General, *The Health Consequences of Smoking: The Changing Cigarette* (Washington, D.C.: Government Printing Office, 1981), p. 99.

33. The Pooling Project Research Group, *Journal of Chronic Diseases* 31 (1978):201.

34. H. M. Annis, "Patterns of Intra-familial Drug Use," *British Journal of Addiction* 69 (1974):361.

35. P. S. Larson, H. B. Haig and Silvette, *Tobacco: Experimental and Clinical Studies* (Baltimore: Williams and Wilkins, 1961).

36. M. E. Jarvick, "Tobacco Smoking in Monkeys," *Annals of the New York Academy of Science* 142 (1967):280.

37. B. Silverstein, *An Addiction Explanation of Cigarette-Induced Relaxation* (Ph.D. dissertation: Columbia University, 1976), pp. 1–68.

38. E. Jones, *Sigmund Freud: Life and Work*, 3 vols. (London: Hogarth Press, 1953), p. 339.

39. R. A. Krumholz, R. B. Chevalier and J. C. Ross, "Changes in Cardiopulmonary Functions Related to Abstinence from Smoking," *Annals of Internal Medicine* 62 (1965):197–207.

40. Surgeon General, *Smoking and Health*, chap. 5, p. 25.

41. Saul M. Schiffman, "The Tobacco Withdrawal Syndrome," in *Cigarette Smoking as a Dependence Process*, ed. N. A. Krasnegor (Washington, D.C.: Government Printing Office, 1979), pp. 158–184.

42. Surgeon General, *Smoking and Health*, chap. 22, p. 10.

43. James I, *A Counterblaste to Tobacco* (London: 1604).

44. Count E. C. Corti, *A History of Smoking* (London: Harrap, 1931), p. 119.

Chapter 5

1. Harold T. Hyman, *An Integrated Practice of Medicine* (Philadelphia: W. B. Saunders Co., 1946), p. 332.
2. U.S., Centers for Disease Control, *Morbidity and Mortality Weekly Report: Annual Summary, 1981,* 54 (October 30, 1982):39.
3. *Ibid.,* p. 39.
4. U.S., Centers for Disease Control, *Morbidity and Mortality Weekly Report* 31 (March 26, 1982):138.
5. B. Frank Polk, "PID: How to Track Down Its Cause," *Patient Care* 17 (1983):81.
6. J. W. Curran, "Economic Consequences of Pelvic Inflammatory Disease in the United States," *American Journal of Obstetrics and Gynecology* 138 (1980):848.
7. *Ibid.*
8. *Ibid.*
9. L. Forslin, F. Viking, and D. Danielson, "Changes in the Incidence of Acute Gonococcal and Nongonococcal Salpingitis," *British Journal of Venereal Disease* 54 (1978):247.
10. Polk, "PID," p. 109.
11. Sylvanus M. Duvall, "Fiction and Facts About Sex," *Reader's Digest* (June 1960), p. 128.
12. Hyman, *An Integrated Practice of Medicine,* p. 332.
13. Quoted by J. S. Habgood, "Societies' Responses," in *Sexually Transmitted Diseases,* ed. R. D. Catterall and C. S. Nicol (London: Academic Press, 1976), pp. 257–258.

Chapter 6

1. C. S. Lewis, *The Four Loves* (New York: Harcourt, Brace, Jovanovich, 1960), p. 177.
2. *Ibid.*
3. *Ibid.,* p. 183.
4. Carl Jung, *Modern Man in Search of a Soul* (New York: Harcourt, Brace and Co., Inc., 1933), p. 260.
5. Erich Fromm, *Psychoanalysis and Religion* (New Haven: Yale University Press, 1950), pp. 86–87.
6. "Sex in Modern Life," *Current Medical Digest,* September 1961, p. 55.
7. Luke 15:11–32.
8. Ronald M. Deutsch, *The Key to Feminine Response in Marriage* (New York: Random House, 1967), pp. 24–25.
9. Herbert J. Miles, *Sexual Happiness in Marriage* (Grand Rapids: Zondervan Publishing House, 1967).
10. Tim and Beverly LaHaye, *The Act of Marriage* (Grand Rapids: Zondervan Corporation, 1976).
11. Ed Wheat, M.D., and Gaye Wheat, *Intended for Pleasure,* rev. ed. (Old Tappan, N.J.: Fleming H. Revell Co., 1981).
12. Deutsch, *Key to Feminine Response in Marriage,* pp. 4–5.
13. LaHaye and LaHaye, *Act of Marriage,* pp. 117–118.
14. Wheat and Wheat, *Intended for Pleasure,* p. 117.

Chapter 7

1. Sari Staver, "The Agony of AIDS: An MD's Battle," *American Medical News*, August 5, 1983, p. 13. Copyright 1983, *American Medical News*. Reprinted with permission.
2. *Ibid.*
3. *Ibid.*, p. 16.
4. *Ibid.*
5. U.S., Centers for Disease Control, "Update: Acquired Immunodeficiency Syndrome (AIDS)—United States," *Morbidity and Mortality Weekly Report* 32 (August 5, 1983):389.
6. I. Bieber et al., *Homosexuality: A Psychoanalytic Study* (New York: Basic Books, 1962).
7. G. Westwood, *A Minority* (London: Longmans, 1960).
8. M. T. Saghir and E. Robins, *Male and Female Homosexuality: A Comprehensive Investigation* (Baltimore: Williams and Wilkins, 1973).
9. L. H. Silverman et al., "An Experimental Study of Aspects of the Psychoanalytic Theory of Male Homosexuality," *Journal of Abnormal Psychology* 82 (1973):178–188.
10. Saghir and Robins, *Male and Female Homosexuality*.
11. Bieber et al., *Homosexuality*.
12. Saghir and Robins, *Male and Female Homosexuality*.
13. Bieber et al., *Homosexuality*.
14. L. B. Apperson and W. G. McAdoo, Jr., "Parental Factors in the Childhood of Homosexuals," *Journal of Abnormal Psychology* 73 (1968):201–206.
15. D. J. West, *Homosexuality Re-Examined* (Minneapolis: University of Minnesota Press, 1977), p. 96.
16. *Ibid.*
17. A. P. Bell and M. S. Weinberg, *Homosexualities: A Study of Diversity Among Men and Women* (New York: Simon and Schuster, 1978).
18. West, *Homosexuality Re-Examined*, p. 163.
19. Lee Birk, "The Myth of Classical Homosexuality," in *Homosexual Behavior*, ed. Judd Marmor (New York: Basic Books, Inc., 1980).
20. Judd Marmor, "Clinical Aspects of Male Homosexuality," in *Homosexual Behavior*, ed. Judd Marmor (New York: Basic Books, Inc., 1980), pp. 266–277.
21. Saghir and Robins, *Male and Female Homosexuality*.
22. Bell and Weinberg, *Homosexualities*.

Chapter 8

1. R. Dagher, M. L. Selzer, and J. Lapides, "Carcinoma of the Penis and the Anti-Circumcision Crusade," *Journal of Urology* 110 (1973):79–80.
2. A. L. Wolbarst, "Circumcision and Penile Cancer," *Lancet* 1 (1932):150–153.
3. E. Leiter and A. M. Lefkovits, "Circumcision and the Penile Carcinoma," *New York State Journal of Medicine* 75 (1975):1520.
4. Dagher, Selzer, and Lapides, "Carcinoma of the Penis," pp. 79–80; M. Riveros and R. Gorostiaga, "Cancer of the Penis," *Archives of Surgery* 85 (1962):377–382; and G. J. Hardner et al., "Carcinoma of the Penis:

Analysis of Therapy in 100 Consecutive Cases," *Journal of Urology* 108 (1972):428–430.

5. J. C. Paymaster and P. Gangadharan, "Cancer of the Penis in India," *Journal of Urology* 97 (1967):110–113.

6. M. Kochen and S. McCurdy, "Circumcision and the Risk of Cancer of the Penis," *American Journal of Diseases of Children* 134 (1980):484–486.

7. Committee on Fetus Newborn, "Report on the Ad Hoc Task Force on Circumcision," *Pediatrics* 56 (1975):610.

8. *Ibid.*

9. W. K. C. Morgan, *Medical Journal of Australia* 7 (1967):1102–1103.

10. W. K. C. Morgan, *Journal of the American Medical Association* 193 (1965):223–224.

11. Dagher, Selzer, and Lapides, "Carcinoma of the Penis," p. 79.

12. Edward Wallerstein, *Circumcision: An American Health Fallacy* (New York: Springer Publishing Co., 1980), p. 108.

13. H. Speert, "Circumcision of the Newborn: An Appraisal of Its Present Status," *Obstetrics and Gynecology* 2 (1953):164–172.

14. Kochen and McCurdy, "Circumcision and the Risk of Cancer of the Penis," p. 484.

15. G. W. Kaplan, "Circumcision—An Overview," *Current Problems in Pediatrics* 7 (1977):10.

16. E. Warner and E. Strashin, "Benefits and Risks of Circumcision," *Canadian Medical Association Journal* 125 (1981):967.

17. J. M. Palmer and D. Link, "Impotence Following Anesthesia for Elective Circumcision," *Journal of the American Medical Association* 241 (1979):2635–6.

18. Warner and Strashin, "Benefits and Risks of Circumcision," p. 973.

19. Genesis 17:10–12.

20. F. Gagnon, "Contribution to Study of Etiology and Prevention of Cancer of Cervix of Uterus," *American Journal of Obstetrics and Gynecology* 60 (1950):516.

21. R. Reid et al., "Genital Warts and Cervical Cancer," *Cancer* 50 (1982):377–387.

22. Joseph Katz, "The Question of Circumcision," *International Surgery* 62 (1977):490–492.

23. G. Cansever, "Psychological Effects of Circumcision," *British Journal of Medical Psychology* 38 (1965):321–331.

24. C. W. McMillan, A. E. Weis, A. M. Johnson, "Acquired Coagulation Disorders in Children," *Pediatric Clinics of North America* 19 (1972):1034.

25. L. Emmett Holt, Jr., and Rustin McIntosh, *Holt Pediatrics*, 12th ed. (New York, Appleton-Century-Crofts, Inc., 1953), pp. 125–126.

26. *Ibid.*

27. James B. Wyngaarden and Lloyd H. Smith Jr., ed. *Cecil Textbook of Medicine* (Philadelphia: W. B. Saunders Co., 1982), p. 1003.

28. J. J. Corrigan Jr., "The Hemorrhagic Disorders," in *Practice of Pediatrics*, 3 vols., ed. V. C. Kelly (Hagerstown, Md.: Harper and Row, Pubs., 1976) 3: chap. 68, p. 7.

29. Moses Maimonides, *The Guide for the Perplexed* (New York: Dover Publications, 1956), p. 378.

30. "The Enigma of Circumcision," *Commentary* 43 (January 1967):52.

31. Quoted by Charles Weis, "A Worldwide Survey of the Current Practice of Milah (Ritual Circumcision)," *Jewish Social Studies*, January 1962, p. 38.
32. Wallerstein, *Circumcision*, p. 157.
33. Weis, "Worldwide Survey of the Current Practice of Milah," p. 31.
34. Speert, "Circumcision of the Newborn," p. 169.
35. Weis, "Worldwide Survey of the Current Practice of Milah," p. 47.
36. Acts 15:22–30.
37. Deuteronomy 10:12,16; Jeremiah 4:4; Romans 2:28–29; 4:11; Galatians 6:13–15.

Chapter 9

1. S. V. Kasl, A. S. Evans, and J. C. Neiderman, "Psychosocial Risk Factors in the Development of Infectious Mononucleosis," *Psychosomatic Medicine* 41 (1979):445.
2. D. Trichopoulos, "Psychological Stress and Fatal Heart Attack: The Athens (1981) Earthquake Natural Experiment," *Lancet* 1 (1983):441.
3. R. Liedtke, H. Freyberger, and S. Zepf, "Personality Features of Persons with Ulcerative Colitis," in *Proceedings of the Eleventh European Conference on Psychosomatic Research* (Basel: Karger, 1977).
4. R. Murison and E. Isaksen, "Biological and Psychological Basis of Gastric Ulceration," in *Biological and Psychological Basis of Psychosomatic Disease*, ed. H. Ursin and R. Murison (Oxford, England: Pergamon Press, 1980).
5. I. Pilowshy, D. Spalding, J. Shaw, and P. I. Korner, "Hypertension and Personality," *Psychosomatic Medicine* 35 (1973):50; M. D. Esler et al., "Mild High-Renin Essential Hypertension: Neurogenic Human Hypertension?" *New England Journal of Medicine* 296 (1977):405.
6. R. Adler, K. MacRitchie, and G. L. Engle, "Psychologic Process and Ischemic Stroke (Occlusive Cerebrovascular Disease): I. Observations on 32 Men with 35 Strokes," *Psychosomatic Medicine* 33 (1971):1.
7. J. J. Lynch et al., "Psychological Aspects of Cardiac Arrhythmia," *American Heart Journal* 93 (1977):645.
8. F. I. Backus and D. L. Dudley, "Observations of Psychosocial Factors and Their Relationship to Organic Disease," in Z. J. Lipowski et al., eds. *Psychosomatic Medicine: Current Trends and Clinical Applications* (New York: Oxford University Press, 1977), p. 196.
9. J. H. Medalie et al., "Angina Pectoris Among 10,000 Men: 5 Year Incidence and Univariate Analysis," *American Journal of Medicine* 55 (1973):583.
10. R. L. Gallon, ed., *The Psychosomatic Approach to Illness* (New York: Elsevier Biomedical, 1982), pp. 168–172.
11. *Ibid.*
12. *Ibid.*
13. B. M. Mandebrote and E. D. Wittkower, "Emotional Factors in Grave's Disease," *Psychosomatic Medicine* 17 (1955):109.
14. S. P. Stein and E. Charles, "Emotional Factors in Juvenile Diabetes Mellitus: A Study of Early Life Experience of Adolescent Diabetics," *American Journal of Psychiatry* 128 (1971):56.
15. Y. Nakai et al., "Alexithymic Features of the Patients with Chronic Pancreatitis," *Proceedings of the Fourth Congress of the International College of Psychosomatic Medicine* (Basel: Karger, 1977).

16. Yukihiro Ago et al., "Psychosomatic Studies of Allergic Disorders," *Proceedings of the Fourth Congress of the International College of Psychosomatic Medicine* (Basel: Karger, 1977).

17. R. F. Solomon and R. H. Moos, "The Relationship of Personality to the Presence of Rheumatoid Factor in Asymptomatic Relatives of Patients with Rheumatoid Arthritis," *Psychosomatic Medicine* 27 (1965):350.

18. Backus and Dudley, "Observations of Psychosocial Factors," p. 196.

19. Kasl, Evans, and Neiderman, "Psychosocial Risk Factors," p. 445.

20. T. H. Holmes, "Psychosocial and Psychophysiological Studies of Tuberculosis," in *Physiological Correlates of Psychological Disorders*, ed. R. R. Greenfield (Madison: University of Wisconsin, 1962), pp. 239–255.

21. R. J. Meyer and R. J. Haggerty, "Streptococcal Infections in Families: Factors Altering Individual Susceptibility," *Pediatrics* 29 (1962):539.

22. A. M. Jacobson, T. C. Manschrech, and E. Silverberg, "Behavioral Treatment for Raynaud's Disease: A Comparative Study with Long-Term Follow-Up," *American Journal of Psychiatry* 136 (1979):844.

23. R. Otto and I. R. MacKay, "Psychosocial and Emotional Disturbance in Systemic Lupus Erythematosis," *Medical Journal of Australia* 2 (1967):488.

24. R. L. Horne and R. S. Picard, "Psychosocial Risk Factors for Lung Cancer," *Psychosomatic Medicine* 41 (1979):503.

25. S. Lehrer, "Life Change and Gastric Cancer," *Psychosomatic Medicine* 42 (1980):499.

26. T. J. Jacobs and E. Charles, "Life Events and the Occurrence of Cancer in Children," *Psychosomatic Medicine* 42 (1980):11.

27. R. B. Shekelle et al., "Psychological Depression and 17-year Risk of Death from Cancer," *Psychosomatic Medicine* 43 (1981):117.

Chapter 10

1. William Sadler, *Practice of Psychiatry* (St. Louis: C. V. Mosby Co., 1953), p. 1008.

2. *Macbeth*, V. iii. 38.

3. *Macbeth*, V. iii. 40.

4. Henry C. Link, *The Way to Security* (Garden City, N.Y.: Doubleday & Co., 1951), p. 52.

Chapter 11

1. Dale Carnegie, *How to Stop Worrying and Start Living* (New York: Simon and Schuster, 1948), p. 101.

2. S. J. Young et al., "Psychiatric Illness and the Irritable Bowel Syndrome," *Gastroenterology* 70 (1976):162.

3. Stanley L. Robbins and Ramzi S. Cotran, *Pathologic Basis of Disease*, 2nd ed. (Philadelphia: W. B. Saunders Co., 1979), p. 985.

4. S. Zisook and R. A. DeVaul, "Emotional Factors in Inflammatory Bowel Disease," *Southern Medical Journal* 70 (1977):716.

5. Robbins and Cotran, *Pathologic Basis of Disease*, p. 986.

6. Adaptation, reprinted by permission of the publisher from "Hostility, CHD Incidence and Total Mortality: A 25-year Follow-Up Study of 255 Physicians," by J. C. Barefoot, W. G. Dahlstrom, and R. B. Williams, *Psychosomatic Medicine* 45:61. Copyright 1983 by Elsevier Science Publishing Co., Inc.

7. H. Weiner, *Physiology of Hypertension* (New York: Elsevier, 1979).
8. Colossians 3:5 (NIV), 8–10 (MOFFATT), 12–14 (NIV).

Chapter 13

1. Lawrence C. Kolb, *Modern Clinical Psychiatry* (Philadelphia: W. B. Saunders Co., 1977), pp. 548–606.
2. Henry C. Link, *What Life Should Mean to You* (Boston: Little, Brown and Co., 1931), p. 258.
3. Edwin Markham, "Outwitted," *Poems of Edwin Markham* (New York: Harper and Brothers, 1950), p. 18.

Chapter 14

1. Based on a chart that appeared in *New York State Health News*, February, 1955.
2. *New York State Health News* (February 1955), p. 9.
3. Jay Hollman, "Type A Behavior is a Spiritual Disease." Reprinted with permission from the *Christian Medical Society Journal*, Volume XII, Number 4, 1982 (p. 5). The Christian Medical Society is a fellowship of Christian physicians and dentists representing Jesus Christ in and through medicine and dentistry. P.O. Box 689, Richardson, Texas 75080.
4. "Psychoneuroendocrine Aspects of Mental Work as Related to Type A Behavior," in *Biological and Psychological Basis of Psychosomatic Disease*, ed. H. Ursin and R. Murison (Oxford: Pergamon Press, 1980).
5. J. Friedman, "The Modification of Type A Behavior in Post-Infarction Patients," *American Heart Journal* 97 (1979):551.
6. Hollman, "Type A Behavior," pp. 6–7.
7. *Ibid.*, pp. 4–10.
8. *Ibid.*

Chapter 15

1. J. S. Heisel, "Life Changes as Etiologic Factors in Juvenile Arthritis," *Journal of Psychosomatic Research* 17 (1972):411–420.
2. A. Amkraut and G. F. Solomon, "From the Symbolic Stimulus to the Pathophysiologic Response: Immune Mechanisms," *International Journal of Psychiatry in Medicine* 5 (1974):541–563.
3. G. F. Solomon, "Emotional and Personality Factors in the Onset and Course of Autoimmune Disease, Particularly Rheumatoid Arthritis," in *Psychoneuroimmunology*, ed. R. Adler (New York: Academic Press, 1981), pp. 174–175.
4. Loring T. Swaim, *Arthritis, Medicine, and Spiritual Laws: Power Beyond Science* (Philadelphia: Chilton Co., 1962).
5. Based on data from R. H. Rahe and M. Romo, "Recent Life Changes and the Onset of Myocardial Infarction and Coronary Death in Helsinki," in *Life* p. 111; and T. Theorell and R. H. Rahe, "Psychosocial Characteristics of Subjects with Myocardial Infarction in Stockholm," p. 96. In *Life, Stress and Illness*, ed. E. K. E. Gunderson and R. H. Rahe, 1974. Courtesy of Charles C. Thomas, Publisher, Springfield, Illinois.

Chapter 16

1. *Heart Facts 1984* (Dallas, Tex.: American Heart Association, 1984), p. 3. © Reproduced with permission. American Heart Association.
2. Adapted from *Handbook of Heart Terms*, National Heart, Lung and Blood Institute.
3. Data from Osmo Turpeinen, "Effect of Cholesterol-Lowering Diet on Mortality from Coronary Heart Disease and Other Causes," *Circulation* 59 (1979):2–3.
4. T. Gordon and W. B. Kannel, "Obesity and Cardiovascular Disease: The Framingham Study," *Clinics in Endocrinology and Metabolism* 5 (1976):367.
5. W. B. Kannel and T. Gordon, "Physiological and Medical Concomitants of Obesity: The Framingham Heart Study," in *Obesity in America* (Washington: Government Printing Office, 1979), p. 125.
6. G. A. Bray, "Effect of Caloric Restriction on Energy Expenditure in Obese Patients," *Lancet* 2 (1969):397–98.
7. Harold Gretzinger, "No Time to Waste," *Christian Life* (February, 1949).
8. J. L. Gordon, D. E. Bowyer, D. W. Evans, and M. J. Mitchinson, "Human Platelet Reactivity During Stressful Diagnostic Procedures," *Journal of Clinical Pathology* 26 (1973):960.

Chapter 17

1. "Childhood Aspects of Psychophysiological Disorders," in *Phenomenology and Treatment of Psychophysiological Disorders*, ed. W. E. Fann et al. (New York: Spectrum Publications, 1979), p. 183.
2. T. Luparello et al., "Influence of Suggestion on Airway Reactivity in Asthmatic Subjects," *Psychosomatic Medicine* 30 (1969):819.
3. T. J. Luparello et al., "The Interaction of Psychologic Stimuli and Pharmacologic Agents in Airway Reactivity in Asthmatic Subjects," *Psychosomatic Medicine* 5 (1970):500.
4. K. Purcell et al., "Effect on Asthma in Children of Experimental Separation from the Family," *Psychosomatic Medicine* 31 (1969):144.
5. J. Brod, in *Society, Stress, and Disease*, ed. L. Levy, 3 vols. (London: Oxford University Press, 1971).
6. R. P. Forsyth, "Blood Pressure Responses to Long Term Avoidance Schedules in the Restrained Rhesus Monkey," *Psychosomatic Medicine* 31 (1969):300.
7. R. P. Forsyth, "Regional Blood-Flow Changes during 72-Hour Avoidance Schedules in the Monkey," *Science* 173 (1971):546.
8. J. P. Henry, J. P. Meehan, and P. M. Stephens, "The Use of Psychosocial Stimuli to Induce Prolonged Systolic Hypertension in Mice," *Psychosomatic Medicine* 29 (1967):408.
9. Backus and Dudley, "Observations of Psychosocial Factors and Their Relationship to Organic Disease," in Z. J. Lipowski et al., eds. *Psychosomatic Medicine: Current Trends and Clinical Applications* (New York: Oxford University Press, 1977), p. 196.

Chapter 18

1. Dale Carnegie, *How to Stop Worrying and Start Living* (New York: Simon & Schuster, 1948), pp. 253–254.

2. William Sadler, *Practice of Psychiatry* (St. Louis: C. V. Mosby Co., 1953), pp. 1012–1013.
3. William Cullen Bryant, "Thanatopsis."

Chapter 19

1. Quoted in Sheldon Vanauken, *A Severe Mercy* (New York: Bantam Books, Inc., 1977), p. 189.
2. *Ibid.*, p. 123.

Chapter 20

1. Frederick Langbridge, "A Cluster of Quiet Thoughts," Religious Tract Society.
2. T. R. Miller, "Psychophysiologic Aspects of Cancer," *Cancer* 39 (1977):414.
3. C. P. Kimball, "A Predictive Study of Adjustment to Cardiac Surgery," *Journal of Thoracic and Cardiovascular Surgery* 58 (1969):891.
4. R. B. Shekelle et al., "Psychological Depression and 17-year Risk of Death from Cancer," *Psychosomatic Medicine* 43 (1981):117.
5. *A Scientific Report on What Hope Does for Man* (New York: New York State Heart Assembly).
6. John Bunyan, *Grace Abounding to the Chief of Sinners* (Philadelphia: J. J. Woodward, 1928), p. 148.
7. Dietrich Bonhoeffer, *The Cost of Discipleship*, 2nd ed., trans. R. H. Fuller; ed. Irmgard Booth (New York: Macmillan Publishing Co., 1959), pp. 122–123.
8. *Ibid.*, p. 123.
9. *Ibid.*

Chapter 21

1. R. Svendsrod, "Locus of Control and Life at Work," in *Biological and Psychological Basis of Psychosomatic Disease*, ed. H. Ursin and R. Murison (Oxford, England: Pergamon Press, 1983), p. 137.
2. Herbert M. Lefcourt, "Locus of Control and Stressful Life Events," in *Stressful Life Events and Their Contexts*, ed. B. S. Dohrenwend and B. P. Dohrenwend (New York: Prodist, 1981), pp. 157–166.
3. J. Rodin, "Managing the Stress of Aging: The Role of Control and Coping," in *Coping and Health*, ed. S. Levine and H. Ursin (New York: Plenum Press, 1980).
4. U. Lundberg and M. Frankenhaeser, "Psychophysiological Reactions to Noise as Modified by Personal Control Over Stimulus Intensity," *Biological Psychology* 6 (1978):51–58.
5. G. W. Comstock and K. B. Partridge, "Church Attendance and Health," *Journal of Chronic Diseases* 25 (1972):665–672.
6. H. G. Thiel, D. Parker, and T. A. Bruce, "Stress Factors and the Risk of Myocardial Infarction," *Journal of Psychosomatic Research* 17 (1973):43–57.
7. Richard J. Foster, *Celebration of Discipline: Paths to Spiritual Growth* (New York: Harper & Row, Pubs., 1978), p. 84.
8. H. Ursin, "Activation, Coping and Psychosomatic," in *Coping Men: A Study*

in Human Psychobiology, ed. H. Ursin, E. Baade, and S. Levine (San Francisco: Academic Press, 1978), p. 223.

9. H. M. Lefcourt, "The Function of the Illusions of Control and Freedom," *American Psychologist* 28 (1973):424–425.

Chapter 22

1. Smiley Blanton, *Love or Perish* (New York: Simon and Schuster, 1956), p. 4.
2. John D. Rockefeller Sr., *Outlook*, October 7, 1905, pp. 300–301.

Chapter 24

1. Carl G. Jung, *Modern Man in Search of a Soul* (New York: Harcourt, Brace and Co., 1933), p. 273.
2. Genesis 21.

Chapter 25

1. William Sadler, *Theory and Practice of Psychiatry* (St. Louis: C. V. Mosby Co., 1936), p. 1075.
2. Carl G. Jung, *Modern Man in Search of a Soul* (New York: Harcourt, Brace and Co., 1933), pp. 260–262.
3. Billy Graham, *Peace With God* (New York: Permabooks, 1955), pp. 124–125.
4. Galatians 4:28–31; 5:17.
5. *Outline of Psychology* (Wheaton, Ill.: Van Kampen Press), p. 453.
6. A. W. Tozer, *The Pursuit of God* (Harrisburg, Pa.: Christian Publications), p. 10.
7. Richard J. Foster, *Celebration of Discipline: Paths to Spiritual Growth* (New York: Harper & Row, Pubs., 1978), p. 148.